Fun as you grow

Minigo

Source ★ Calcium
★ Protéines/Protein
★ Vitamine D/Vitamin D¹

NICOLE DORÉ
DANIELLE LE HÉNAFF

From Tiny Tot to Toddler

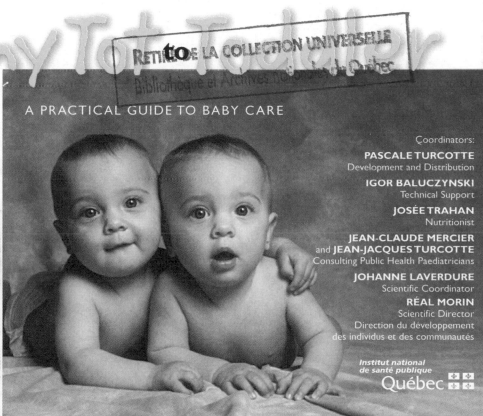

A PRACTICAL GUIDE TO BABY CARE

Coordinators:

PASCALE TURCOTTE
Development and Distribution

IGOR BALUCZYNSKI
Technical Support

JOSÉE TRAHAN
Nutritionist

JEAN-CLAUDE MERCIER
and **JEAN-JACQUES TURCOTTE**
Consulting Public Health Paediatricians

JOHANNE LAVERDURE
Scientific Coordinator

RÉAL MORIN
Scientific Director
Direction du développement
des individus et des communautés

*Institut national
de santé publique*
Québec

First edition: 1988. Revised, expanded editions: 1995 and 2003.

From Tiny Tot to Toddler: a Practical Guide to Baby Care and the French version *Mieux vivre avec notre enfant de la naissance à deux ans, guide pratique pour les mères et les pères* is given free of charge to Quebec parents upon birth of their child. The guide is also sold in bookstores and Publications du Québec outlets. In autumn 2004, the guide will be available online at www.inspq.qc.ca/MieuxVivre (see page 481 for details).

The French version is available on audiocassette from the Magnétothèque de Montréal at 1 800 361-0635.

Braille copies are available from the Institut Nazareth et Louis-Braille: (450) 463-1710.

Brand names of products described in this document are given as examples only.

Legal deposit – 3rd quarter 2004
Bibliothèque nationale du Québec
National Library of Canada
ISBN: 2-551-22511-6
© Institut national de santé publique du Québec

2005 Edition

Editorial team
Johanne Laverdure, Jean-Claude Mercier, Réal Morin, Josée Trahan, Jean-Jacques Turcotte, Pascale Turcotte

Writers
Christiane Auray-Blais, Lucie Baribeau, Louise Beaudry, Céline Belhumeur, France Bilodeau, Julie Boissonneault, Marie-Andrée Bossé, Nicole Boulianne, Isabelle Brabant, Lise Brassard, Marie-Ève Caty, Brigitte Chaput, Isabelle Charbonneau, Aurore Côté, Dominique Cousineau, Rosanne Couture, Jacques Durocher, Sylvie Fortin, Chantal Galarneau, Suzanne Goyette, Julie Guimond, Luce Hamel, Natacha Joubert, Ginette Lamarre, André Lavallière, Michel Lavoie, France Lebrun, Suzanne Lépine, Josée Lespérance, Anne Letarte, Patrick Levallois, Chantal Lévesque, Marie-Joëlle Levesque, Michel Levy, Jean-Claude Mercier, Langis Michaud, Christina Morin, Suzan Palmer, Lina Perron, Denise Phaneuf, Marie-Christine Robin, Diane Sergerie, Isabel Thibault, Lucie Thibodeau, Josée Trahan, Jean-Jacques Turcotte, Pascale Turcotte, Ginette Veilleux

Technical support
Igor Baluczynski

English translation and editing
Traductions Terrance Hughes Inc.
Stevenson & Writers Inc.

Graphic design and computer graphics
Lucie Chagnon

Illustrations
Virginie (Ginny) Armstrong Schaefer

Proofreading
Marie-Josée Allie

Printing
Les imprimeries Quebecor World

Cover photos
Louise Condrain, Health Canada

See pages 476 and 477 for a complete list of collaborators on the 2005 edition.

The 2005 editions of *From Tiny Tot to Toddler* and *Mieux vivre avec notre enfant de la naissance à deux ans* are distributed free of charge to the following to support Quebec parents:

- Prenatal workers at CLSCs;

- General practitioners providing health care to pregnant women and newborns;

- Health care workers at community organizations serving young families;

- Mothers and monitors supporting new mothers through breast-feeding support groups.

The Institut national de santé publique du Québec is proud to present this entirely revised and updated edition of *From Tiny Tot to Toddler: A Practical Guide to Baby Care*. Additions to the book include suggested activities for parents and infants in the section on children's development and more extensive information on fatherhood in the section devoted to the family.

We are committed to promoting the health and well-being of newborns and will continue to update, publish, distribute and develop *From Tiny Tot to Toddler*. In particular, we will ensure that all Quebec parents receive this guide at the time of the birth or adoption of their child.

Scientific rigour is maintained through the collaboration of numerous experts in the fields of child development, nutrition, prevention, child care and support for parents. The experts' contribution continues to enrich the guide's contents, which are constantly reviewed in light of the latest scientific knowledge.

The comments of parents who use *From Tiny Tot to Toddler* also influence the guide's contents and presentation. Help us to give you the information you need in a user-friendly form by filling out and returning the questionnaire on page 478.

Thank you for your collaboration, and happy reading.

Richard Massé, MD
President and CEO
Institut national de santé publique du Québec

Can I raise a glass to my baby's health?

If you care about the health of your child, Éduc'alcool recommends that you avoid drinking during your pregnancy.

This is one of the issues covered in Pregnancy and Drinking: Your Questions Answered, a free brochure that discusses such things as the effect of alcohol on fetal development and how to enjoy an occasional drink while nursing.

The brochure is published jointly by Éduc'alcool, the *Collège des médecins du Québec and the Ministère de la Santé et des Services sociaux du Québec*. Ask your doctor for a copy, order it directly from Éduc'alcool (1-888-ALCOOL-1) or go online to **www.educalcool.qc.ca**.

Éduc▼**alcool**
Moderation is always in good taste.

Foreword

Dear Parents,
This practical guide to baby care is a gift to mark the birth
of your child.

Your baby has arrived.

You will learn to know your child and live with him. Your child is unique and fragile but carries the legacy of the thousands of generations of women and men who have preceded you. His remarkable potential is that of humankind. To achieve his potential fully, he needs you.

Does the task seem daunting to you? Do not worry, for although your child is small, he has surprising resources. You have the necessary skills to become parents. In almost no time, you will establish a strong bond with your newborn. Have confidence in yourselves, seek information calmly and get to know your baby in order to adjust to him.

We have assembled in this guide the answers to the questions that Quebec parents have been asking us for over 25 years. The guide offers the most up-to-date information available. We hope that it will help guide the decisions you will have to make during the first two years of your child's life and that it will help you become unique parents, different from others but fully adapted to your family and culture.

The guide is divided into four sections. The first section provides useful information on your baby and his development. The second section focuses on the needs of each member of the family, with a view to ensuring that the family grows harmoniously. The third section is devoted to breast-feeding and diet. The fourth section offers information on children's health and covers topics ranging from prevention to diseases and first aid. Various resources designed to help you fulfil your role as parents are listed at the back of the guide.

Health professionals are always available to inform you about the care your child needs and the stages in his development. Do not hesitate to consult them. However, remember that you are responsible for making decisions that concern your child.

Becoming a parent is like learning to walk. You may stumble and fall, but you get back on your feet. Give yourself a chance to learn and improve yourself. Above all, take the time to discover the pleasures of being a parent.

Pascale Turcotte, Institut national de santé publique du Québec
Gloria Jeliu, paediatrician, Hôpital Sainte-Justine, Montréal

From Tiny Tot to Toddler 2005 Edition

Your Baby

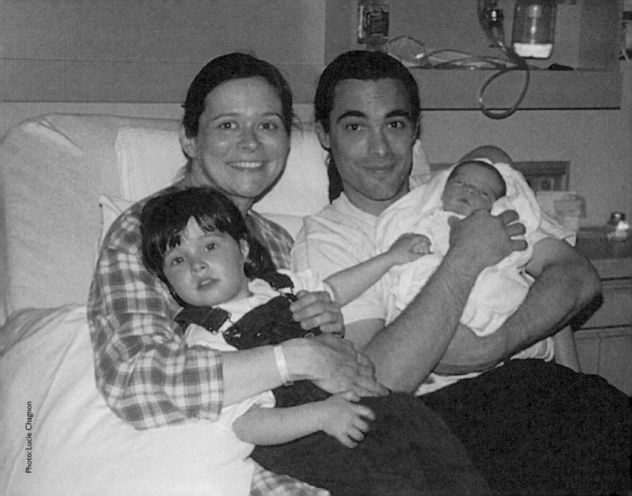

The First Days

Your baby has finally arrived. Who does she look like? Her father? Her mother? A distant relative, perhaps? If you chose international adoption, she probably reminds you of her country of origin. Regardless of who she resembles, your baby is unique. You will discover a lot about her.

To guide you in this wonderful adventure, let us begin by sharing information that is useful during the first few days of your baby's life.

Hospital stay

The usual hospital stay is 2 days after a vaginal birth and 4 days after a Caesarean section. The stay in a birthing centre is roughly 24 hours. More and more hospitals are encouraging mothers and fathers to room-in with their baby, a unique experience. Take advantage of it to familiarize yourself with the routine of taking care of your newborn. Keeping your baby near you, often held against your skin, will make her feel secure and strengthen the mother-child bond. Rooming-in also allows you to nurse the infant on demand. **Babies who nurse during their first hour of life and who nurse frequently afterwards are less susceptible to jaundice and dehydration.**

These first hours are precious. Take advantage of them. However, set aside some time to complete the routine formalities that accompany a birth.

Formalities

The guide *Becoming a Parent,* produced by Communication-Québec in collaboration with the Régie des rentes du Québec, contains information on the essential steps to follow, such as filling out the declaration of birth, requesting leave and benefits, registering the baby for health and drug insurance, planning for educational and day care services, and so on. It also contains a list of important telephone numbers. Consult the guide and **keep it on hand**.

You probably received the guide during a medical examination prior to the birth of your baby. If not, you can obtain a copy from most CLSCs and all Communication-Québec offices. You can also consult *Becoming a Parent* on the Quebec government Web site (www.gouv.qc.ca).

Screening for hereditary metabolic diseases

Shortly after her birth, a blood sample will be taken from your baby to detect certain genetic diseases. Other hereditary metabolic diseases can also be screened. To this end, you will have to take a urine sample **when she is 21 days old**.

Use the kit that you received before you left the hospital or birthing centre, which comprises 2 envelopes. One envelope contains an explanatory brochure, a yellow form to be filled out, a blotter, and a reply envelope. The other envelope contains 2 absorbent pads and an instruction sheet. Read it carefully.

To ensure that the analyses are conducted properly, be sure to follow the instructions.

- **Do not use** disposable wet washcloths to wash your baby's bottom before the sample is taken.

- **Do not apply** cream, oil or powder to her bottom when the sample is taken.

To take the sample, follow the procedure indicated below.

- Insert an absorbent pad (with the plastic film) in the diaper. Watch your baby and withdraw the pad as soon as she urinates. There must **not** be any stool on the absorbent pad.

- Place the urine-soaked pad on the blotting paper and press to moisten it completely on both sides. **If the quantity of urine is insufficient to moisten the blotting paper**, take another sample with the second absorbent pad and again moisten the blotting paper. Then, allow the blotting paper to dry.

- Fill out the information form (yellow sheet). Indicate the baby's approximate weight and whether she is breast-feeding or bottle-feeding. This information will help medical staff to interpret the results. Be sure to check your address and telephone number.

- When the blotting paper is dry, put it in the reply envelope with the yellow form. Put a stamp on the envelope and mail it.

There, that's done! The screening program is voluntary and participation is relatively easy. It makes it possible to detect metabolic diseases, which are caused by proteins or protein derivatives that the body poorly absorbs or assimilates. Parents who submit a urine sample give their baby a chance to benefit from early detection. If the analyses reveal an abnormality, your baby will be offered the necessary medical follow-up. **If everything is normal, you will not be contacted**.

Did you forget? Remember the old adage, "Better late than never." Take the urine sample as soon as you remember it.

The sample is important for your baby's health. To find out more, contact the provincial urinary control program (see "Useful addresses," page 442).

Car safety seats are compulsory

Each year in Quebec, road accidents kill over 1000 children under 7 years of age. Most of these accidents occur near the home. It is essential to use a car safety seat to transport your baby safely as soon as she leaves the hospital or birth centre (see page 359 for more information). Your baby is a precious human being. **Always use a car safety seat**.

Car safety seat for newborns

The car safety seat for newborns surrounds the baby's body and keeps her in a comfortable, semi-recumbent position while supporting her lower back. It is usually designed for children weighing less than 9 kg (20 lb.) or under 66 cm (26 inches) in height. **Carefully read the manufacturer's instructions**.

Adjustment of the straps (or harness) before use

You must adjust the straps (or harness) of the infant's seat according to your baby's size. Make this adjustment before you install the seat in the car. Always refer to the manufacturer's instructions: they are very important. Do not hesitate to ask for assistance from staff before you leave the hospital.

Installing a car safety seat

- **Adjust the strap or harness to the right height.** There are several slots on the back of the seat. Insert the harness straps in the slots just below the baby's shoulders so that the harness covers them.

- **Adjust the strap or harness to the right length.** First, place your baby in the seat and attach the harness by inserting the metal clasp into the buckle or harness latch plate. Make sure that you hear a click. Next, adjust the chest clip or harness tie linking the two harness straps so that it is in the middle of the baby's chest (level with her armpits). **This will prevent her from being ejected from the seat in the event of impact.** Check the adjustment: if you can slide more than one finger between your baby's body and the harness, you must shorten the harness. Of course, you must readjust the harness regularly as your baby grows and when she changes clothes from one season to the next.

- Place the seat in the car with the back facing traffic. **Yes, your child must look toward the back of the vehicle.** In the event of an accident, her head, neck and rib cage will better survive the shock. The safest place to install the car safety seat is in the middle of the back seat of the car, near another passenger. **Never install it on the front seat if your vehicle is**

equipped with an airbag on the passenger side, as it would be dangerous to do so (consult the manufacturer's instructions for more information).

- Make sure that the seat is fully horizontal (your baby should be at a 45° angle, in a semi-recumbent position) so that the baby's head and back are properly supported. If the car seat is overly inclined, place a rolled-up towel under the baby's seat.

- Attach the baby's seat to the car. If it has an independent base, attach the base to the car seat with the seatbelt **or** the Isofix belt or LATCH Universal Children's Restraint Anchorage (UCRA) system (see page 359 for information on the Isofix or LATCH system), then attach the seat to the base. Attach a 1-piece seat by passing the seatbelt through the slots. If the seatbelt is not self-locking, install a metal safety clip (usually sold with

the seat). This will prevent the seat from sliding in the event of impact. Your car owner's manual and the car safety seat manufacturer's instructions indicate all of the manufacturer's recommendations for proper use of the seatbelt and shoulder belt.

Your baby is now ready for her first car ride!

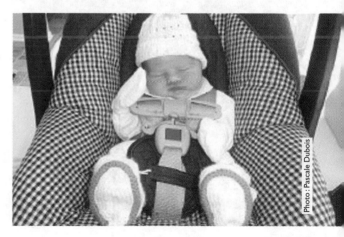

Photo : Pascale Dubois

Characteristics of the Newborn

Fetal position

During his first weeks of life, your baby will often maintain the fetal position with his arms and legs bent.

Apgar score

The Apgar test measures a baby's health immediately after birth and several minutes later. The doctor checks 5 things: heart rate, breathing, muscle tone, reflexes and skin colour. The score ranges from 0 to 2 for each element, with 2 being the best score. A newborn's physical health is considered good if his total score is 8 to 10. A lower score indicates the possible need for intervention or monitoring.

Height and weight

A full-term baby, that is, a baby born after 37 to 42 weeks of pregnancy, is usually between 45 cm and 55 cm in height (18 inches and 21 inches) and weighs between 2500 g and 4300 g (5 lb. and 9 lb.).

Your baby can lose between 5% and 10% of his weight in the first days after birth. This is normal, since he only drinks a small amount of milk at a time. A healthy, full-term baby will regain his birth weight between the eighth and fifteenth day.

Skin

The colour of a newborn's skin ranges from pink to purplish. His hands and feet are sometimes paler and may be bluish for up to 48 hours after birth. His skin may also be mottled because of the cold: his internal thermostat has still not adjusted properly. In most instances, the mottling will disappear once the baby is warm.

Generally speaking, a newborn's skin is smooth, soft and transparent in places. It may be wrinkled and peeling. It is sensitive to cold and heat. When your baby is born, his skin may be covered with a whitish coating that the body absorbs within a few hours or several days. Certain babies and premature infants may be covered with a fine down, called lanugo, which disappears within a few weeks.

Umbilical cord

The white umbilical cord dries up, darkens and falls off on its own, usually between 7 and 20 days after birth, but occasionally as long as a month later (see "Caring for the navel," page 42).

Eye colour

A baby's eyes are grey or blue at birth and take on their permanent colour during the first year. Tears appear when the baby is around 3 or 4 weeks old.

Your baby's head

A baby's head is big and heavy. It needs to be supported when you pick up your baby. The nape of your baby's neck is delicate: make sure that his head turns easily from left to right. If he moves with difficulty and seems to be in pain, he may have a stiff neck. It is recommended that you consult a health professional (see "Who can help your baby?," page 314).

Has the pressure of birth deformed your baby's head? It will regain its rounded shape within a few weeks. At birth, the skull bones have not yet knit

23

together, but are connected by a diamond-shaped membrane called the anterior fontanel. It is located on the top of the head and is soft to the touch and slightly indented when the baby is sitting up. It closes up between the ages of 9 and 18 months.

Caput succedaneum

At birth, a lump called a caput succedaneum (swelling or an accumulation of blood) may be visible under your baby's scalp. It does not in any way harm the brain and disappears without a trace after a few days or weeks.

Genital organs

The area surrounding a baby girl's genital organs is usually swollen for 2 or 3 days after birth. Vernix caseosa, a cheesy-white material, is sometimes present in the vaginal labial folds. Do not remove it since it provides excellent antibacterial protection. A few drops of blood may appear around the vagina during the first week. This mini-menstruation is caused by the surplus of hormones transmitted by the mother before birth. It is not cause for concern.

The testicles of full-term baby boys have usually descended in the scrotum, which is purplish-red. If they have not descended, inform the doctor. The foreskin, a thin fold of skin, sticks to the glans penis (the bulbous tip). Do not forcefully loosen it. It is pointless and harmful to force dilation since it is painful and can injure the baby. Let nature take its course: 90% of boys will be naturally dilated at the age of 3 and some will not be dilated until adolescence. Circumcision is not usually recommended. The operation consists in partially or totalling removing the foreskin and is extremely painful for a newborn. However, it may be done for religious reasons.

Swollen breasts

Newborn boys and girls may have swollen breasts, which may even produce a small amount of milk. Do not touch them. The swelling will go down within a few days.

Skin spots

Some newborns have small pink spots between their eyes, on their eyelids, and on the back of the neck. These spots turn white when touched, become more visible when baby cries and disappear during the first year. Some babies have bluish spots on their bottoms and backs, which disappear before the child reaches the age of 3. Other spots are permanent.

Pimples

Small white pimples occasionally appear on the nose and chin of a newborn, due to the obstruction of the sweat glands: a newborn will not perspire before the beginning of the third week. These little pimples gradually disappear within a few weeks. Do not touch them (see "Milium or milia," page 396).

Jaundice

If your baby's skin is yellow, he probably has "physiological jaundice of the newborn," which affects roughly 60% of healthy full-term babies and 80% of premature babies. Among full-term babies, it usually begins 2 or 3 days after birth, peaks on the third or fourth day, then disappears after the first week. Jaundice in premature babies can last for several weeks.

Physiological jaundice is due to an accumulation in the blood of orange-coloured pigments called bilirubin. The pigments stem from the normal destruction of old red blood cells that are poorly eliminated by the still immature liver. The pigments are responsible for the yellow coloration of the whites of the baby's eyes and his skin.

A newborn also eliminates bilirubin pigments in his stools. Jaundice is more pronounced when the baby does not drink enough and intestinal function is limited.

Jaundice may persist for up to 2 months in some breast-fed infants. The baby develops properly, gains weight, and produces normal stools and urine. This type of jaundice does not cause problems nor does it require treatment. Continue to breast-feed normally. If you are concerned, consult a health professional (see "Who can help your baby?," page 314).

▶ What to do

It is not easy to assess the intensity of a newborn's yellow colouring. Look at your baby's skin and the whites of his eyes. If you find that he is very yellow, consult a CLSC doctor or nurse. If need be, a device that measures skin colour or a blood test will be used to determine the intensity of the jaundice. If the bilirubin level is too high, the doctor may treat the baby with phototherapy lamps in the hospital. **However, most cases of jaundice do not require treatment**.

Make sure that your infant drinks enough milk. Offer him the breast frequently: 8 to 12 nursings in 24 hours are often necessary during the first 2 weeks.

Sneezing

Your baby sneezes often, which is normal. Since the hairs protecting his nostrils are not sufficiently developed, he may sneeze up to 12 times a day to expel secretions in the nose that interfere with breathing. Such sneezing does not necessarily mean that he has a cold.

Hiccups

Your baby may also have the hiccups, especially after nursing. Do not worry, hiccups do not harm him and will stop by themselves within a few minutes.

Keeping your baby warm

Your baby needs to be kept warm, but not overly warm. He must not sweat. If you are comfortable with the room temperature, he will be comfortable, too: between 20°C (68°F) and 24°C (75°F) is sufficient. Use light covers, which you can add or remove, depending on the room temperature. Do not swaddle your baby too tightly.

Urine

A baby who drinks sufficiently urinates regularly. His urine is pale yellow and odourless. During a baby's first week, he will urinate more and more frequently, for example, from the fifth day on, between 5 and 25 times a day (see "Elimination," page 318).

Brick-red spots may appear in your baby's diaper. Do not worry, this is normal. The spots are uric acid crystals mixed with water that are eliminated in the first days of your baby's life.

Is he urinating less frequently than usual and is his urine dark and smelly? He may have a fever, be too warmly dressed, or it may simply be very hot. Increase the number of feedings and give him more water if he is being bottle-fed.

Stools

For 2 or 3 days after birth, your baby's stools will be very dark, black or green, and sticky. Your baby is eliminating residues (meconium) that accumulated in his intestine before birth. Colostrum, protein-rich breast milk, facilitates this process. Subsequently, during the first year, the frequency and consistency of your baby's stools will vary depending on the type of food he eats.

You will gradually learn to recognize your child's normal stools.

During breast-feeding, stools range in colour from golden yellow to greenish-yellow. They are liquid or semi-liquid and smell of sour milk. The stools of babies that are exclusively breast-fed irritate the buttocks less.

A newborn may defecate up to 10 times a day during the first 6 weeks. Most babies then produce from 2 to 5 big stools a day as long as they are only breast-fed, while other babies may have a bowel movement only once a week. If the stools are infrequent but remain soft, there is no cause for concern. Make sure that your baby drinks often and in sufficient quantity, that he wets his diapers and is gaining weight normally (see the table on page 207 and "How baby grows," page 317).

Liquid stools may mean that your infant is suffering from a temporary indisposition (see "Intestinal disorders," page 417). Some medication can cause a change: an iron supplement can produce black or dark brown stools.

Diapers must be changed frequently and it is advantageous to make this a pleasant time. Your baby will certainly like to hear you talking to him or singing him a song. Quiet music, a rattle, pictures on the wall, a mirror or a story book can also distract him and facilitate diaper changing.

If your baby is healthy and is developing normally, do not be overly concerned about his stools.

Stools and solid food

The stools of babies who eat solid food will vary in colour and consistency depending on the menu. When a new food such as a vegetable or fruit is only partially digested, it can soften the stools for several days. The new food can also change their colour: a baby who eats green vegetables may produce green stools. Do not be concerned if you find fragments of fruits or vegetables in your baby's diaper. This occurs frequently and is usually normal. To help your child digest, give him crushed or more finely ground foods.

Constipation

Does your baby strain and turn red when he has a bowel movement? This is normal. Do not be concerned, unless the stools are hard and dry, in which case your baby is constipated (see "Constipation," page 297).

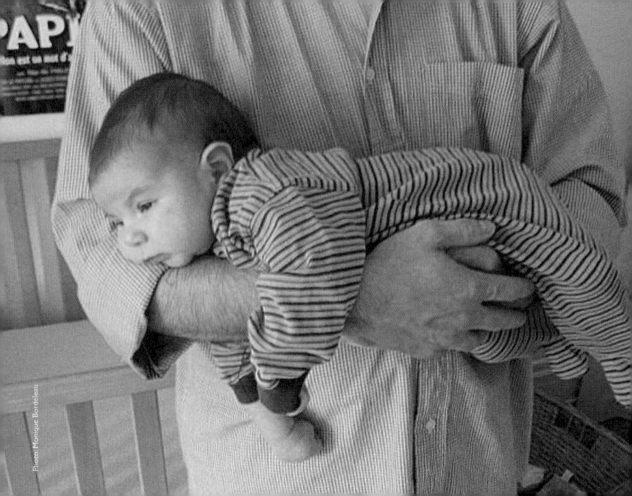

Communicating With Your Baby

At birth, a newborn's brain contains all of the nerve cells that will allow her to mature quickly, although the cells are not fully developed.

Breast-feeding and frequent exchanges with her parents and family circle foster a child's development. She will develop better in a climate of trust and security.

✪ **Golden rule**

To raise your child, you must understand her. To understand her, you must observe her, and admire her as often as possible.

Your baby talks to you

From birth, a baby expresses herself in different ways. She moans, babbles, wriggles about and suckles intensely. If you pay attention to her, you and your baby will communicate quite naturally. Talk to her. Tell her what you are doing when you take care of her. This will not only stimulate her language development but also reassure her. When she hears your gentle words, she will know that she can rely on you.

During her first 2 years, as her brain develops, your baby will absorb what she hears. She will learn to speak by repeating the sounds and words that she hears (see "Frequently asked questions on language," page 76).

Crying

Long before your baby acquires speech, crying is one of the first forms of communication. All babies cry, some more often than others, depending on their temperament. The intensity of crying depends on the baby's need. While it may not be obvious initially, you will quickly learn to recognize your baby's different cries and to understand what they mean:

- I'm hungry!
- My diaper is dirty!
- I've got gas!
- I need affection!
- I want your attention!
- I need to burp or I need my pacifier!
- Or quite simply, I'm having a bad day!
- I'm tired!
- I'm too hot or too cold!
- I'm bored!
- I want to play with you!

Sometimes it will be impossible to find the reason for your baby's crying. Try to comfort her anyway. During her first months of life, your baby is incapable of understanding the notion of time and tolerating discomfort. She needs your prompt, warm response. In this way, she will develop a sense of security and trust you.

During the first months, do not hesitate to respond promptly to your baby's crying (see "Consoling your baby," page 34). You will not spoil your child by responding quickly to her crying. She will learn that you are attentive to her messages and prepared to satisfy her needs.

Speak to her, touch her, make sure she has eaten enough, that she is warm and dry and that she is not sick. If need be, take her temperature (see "Fever," page 402). Your understanding of your baby's needs and your response to her should enable your child to regain her sense of well-being and satisfaction.

When she is a bit older, your child may cry because she misses you or wants the pleasure of interacting with you. Her behaviour as soon as you arrive will help you understand the message. It is up to you to determine the appropriate response at that time. For example, if your baby wants to play in the middle of the night, you must guide her so that she continues to sleep by limiting your intervention and clearly communicating this instruction to her (see "The need for supervision and discipline," page 79).

Starting at the age of 6 months, some babies occasionally cry so hard that they convulse and turn blue, in what is called a **breath-holding spell**. The episode lasts less than a minute. The baby

33

shrieks until she stops breathing for several seconds. She pales or turns blue, no longer sits up and can fall. Parents are initially concerned, but when they recognize that their child's reaction does not threaten her health they must stay calm and avoid worrying. Your child will quickly start breathing again on her own. Do not leave her, wait until she calms down and reassure her. However, if the breath-holding spell occurs before the age of 4 months or it lasts for more than a minute, see a physician.

Excessive crying (colic)

Your baby is crying loudly and has been crying steadily for over 3 hours, especially at the end of the day or in the evening and often at the same time of day. Her face is red, her fists are clenched and her legs are folded over her stretched, swollen tummy. She may have gas. It is very hard to console her. Between bouts of crying, she is cheerful and seems satisfied. She is gaining weight normally.

Colic is excessive crying by a healthy baby. Little is known about its causes. Colic is part of the process of the child's adaptation to her new environment and stems from her sensitivity. Breast-fed babies can also suffer from it. It occurs around the age of 2 to 3 weeks and often disappears toward the third or fourth month. The most difficult period occurs around the sixth week.

▶ What to do

Make sure that your baby is not hungry, hot or cold, or that she needs a clean diaper or to burp. Also ensure that she is not feverish and that she is drinking just the right amount of milk. Try to console her.

Consoling your baby

- Seek a calm environment.
- Speak softly to your baby, play soft music and touch her. Place her on your stomach with her skin against yours, in a warm place. Massage or caress her.

- Many babies calm down while nursing. In addition to feeding her, it can also console her.

- Move her around, walk around with her, and rock her. A walk in a stroller or a car trip is often effective. Think of the ventral sac (see "Front or back infant carrier," page 364).

- Give her a bath. Some babies adore water.

- Hold your baby in the "anti-colic" position. Put her on her stomach on your forearm with her back against your stomach and her head in the crook of your elbow. Support your forearm on your abdomen with your hand between her legs (see picture on page 30).

If your baby is inconsolable

Seek help. When you are tired or exasperated, it is good to rely on your partner or someone else you trust who can give you a hand. Have someone replace you and get out of the house to take a break from your baby's crying. When you come back, you will be able to transmit a sense of calm rather than agitation.

What if you are feeling overwhelmed but have no one to replace you? Put your baby in a safe place, for example, in her bed, close the door and go away from the room for several minutes. You need a break. Seek help immediately from a babysitter, a relative, a doctor, your CLSC, a volunteer centre or La ligne parents (see "Useful addresses," page 440). **Never shake an infant**: you could cause permanent brain injury or even kill her.

An important reminder

Consult a physician to obtain a proper diagnosis. Medication to treat colic is not usually recommended.

Intense crying can also be a sign of allergies or other causes (see "Allergy to cow's milk," page 300).

Touch

Touch is the first sense that develops in the uterus and is constantly called into play during pregnancy, when your baby rubs against the uterine wall, you rub your abdomen to make contact with her, and so on. After birth, breast-feeding is a form of complete, warm, reassuring and satisfying contact.

Touch satisfies a need as essential as drinking and eating. It is a form of communication that the newborn appreciates. The way you rock her, hold her against your chest or on your shoulder, comforts her. Your caresses calm her and can soothe her crying. Kissing your baby fosters her awareness of life. Touching her communicates your love.

If you like giving massages, your baby will be delighted. It is easy to massage a newborn, who will often appreciate it a great deal. Massaging your baby relaxes her, helps her body to function properly, and fosters her development. Moreover, in this way, you will learn more quickly to recognize her gestures, which will bolster your confidence in your parenting skills.

For a successful massage, follow these basic guidelines:

- Wait until your baby is wide awake and receptive, preferably between feedings.

- Make sure that the room is warm and comfortable.

- It is best to sit on the floor.

- Massage your baby gently but firmly with the entire palm of your hand to avoid tickling her.

- Use vegetable oil such as sunflower-seed or other oil warmed in your hands to ensure pleasant contact. Test it on a small area of the baby's body to ensure that she is not allergic to it.

- Maintain a relaxed attitude and be attentive to your baby's preferences.

You can begin the massage on your baby's temples or the soles of her feet. Repeat the gestures that appear to be good for her, and follow your intuition. To obtain additional information, there are good books on baby massage or contact your CLSC. Baby massage workshops are organized for parents wishing to broaden their knowledge of the subject.

If you have trouble planning a set period for the massage, take advantage of bath time. Wash your baby with your hands but without a washcloth, then take the time to rub her body with cream. She will appreciate the contact and the time that you devote to her.

Taste and smell

A newborn already possesses a sense of taste and smell. Very early on, she is able to recognize her mother by her smell. The odour of milk draws her to the nipple to satisfy her hunger. Sucking gives her an intense feeling of well-being. The taste of breast milk can vary depending on the mother's diet. This exposure helps to develop her sense of taste.

Hearing

Your baby can hear at birth, and even before. She is especially sensitive to the human voice, perhaps because she has often heard it in the womb. She can turn her head in the direction from which the sound comes. Familiar sounds reassure your baby. Calling her in a soft voice will often calm her. Loud noise will startle and disturb her. Experiment with sounds to see whether or not your baby can hear properly. In case of doubt, see your doctor.

The ears of newborns can protrude somewhat. Nothing can be corrected at this age. Talk to your doctor about it before your child starts school.

Eyesight

As soon as she is born, a baby is able to clearly see faces within 30 cm (12 inches) of her eyes. Sight is a primary means of communication for all babies. At the age of 1 month, the baby will seek out and look at light that is not too intense. At the age of 2 months, babies begin to perceive colours and can start to track their parents and slow-moving objects. A baby's limited field of vision increases to equal that of an adult's around the age of 1 year. As eye muscle control is not established before the age of 6 months, infants may occasionally become cross-eyed. See your doctor or an optometrist if the problem persists beyond the age of 6 months.

A child with a vision problem is not likely to complain. From the baby's perspective, her vision is normal. Almost 25% of children under the age of 6 have eye problems; only 15% consult an optometrist or ophthalmologist. Any vision problem should be corrected before the age of 8 or it will become permanent and may affect education and employment.

Early signs of impaired vision in a child:

- Doesn't follow moving objects with her eyes.
- Blinks often.
- Is very sensitive to light, eyes water a great deal.
- Hides one eye to look or focuses by turning her head.
- Cries when you cover one eye.
- Bumps into things and has difficulty getting her bearings.
- One eye seems different from the other (after 6 months of age).

YOUR CHILD HAS BEAUTIFUL EYES…

BUT ARE THEY GOOD?

An eye health and vision examination by your optometrist will give you the answer.

This examination is recommended at the age of 3, or at any previous age if the child shows signs of vision problems or eye disease, or if there are hereditary issues in the family.

Eye health… It's important!

 Association

DES
OPTOMÉTRISTES
DU
QUÉBEC

www.aoqnet.qc.ca

Caring for Baby

Picking up your baby

New parents should not be afraid of picking up their baby. Your baby is not as fragile as he seems but needs to be handled gently and lovingly. Always support his head and back until he is roughly 3 months of age. You can wrap him in a small blanket when you pick him up. Babies like to be rocked since it reminds them of the movements they felt in the womb.

Hold your baby often. **You will not spoil your child by satisfying his needs for comforting and love**.

Caring for the navel

Wash around the umbilical cord every day until the navel has healed. Use a cotton swab moistened with lukewarm water to gently wash the area. Do not use rubbing alcohol since this will delay the detachment of the cord. Gently sponge the area with a dry cotton swab. The navel must always be dry. Do not cover it with the diaper or a compress. Make sure that the diaper is always folded below the navel to prevent irritation.

The umbilical cord can stay partially detached for 2 or 3 days and leave traces of blood on the baby's diaper or clothing. Once it falls off, a few drops of blood may flow from the scar when your baby cries. This is not dangerous and the navel will heal by itself.

A clean umbilical cord does not have a foul odour or discharge. In case of doubt, see a health professional (see "Who can help your baby?", page 314).

The baby's bath

Everyday baby care is a source of pleasure and relaxation. Bath time is a wonderful opportunity for mothers and fathers to get to know their baby and strengthen their emotional bonds through speech, sight and touch.

At home, continue to give your baby his bath as you were taught to do at the hospital or birthing centre. You can bathe your baby with a washcloth or directly in the bathtub. If the water is the right temperature, that is, body temperature, your newborn should not be uncomfortable. Some parents prefer to wash their baby with a washcloth until his navel has healed, although bathing him in the bathtub poses no additional risk of infection. Moreover, a bath allows your baby to stay warmer.

When to bathe your baby

Choose the time that suits you. Any time of the day is fine as long as your baby is awake. During the first 15 days of your baby's life, do not wash him more than 2 or 3 times a week. However, wash his face, neck, bottom and genital organs every day.

Preparation

Before you undress your baby, assemble the following items:

- a washcloth and a towel;
- a blanket in which to wrap him;
- clean clothes;
- a diaper;

- unscented mild white soap with neutral pH, if need be;

- unscented moisturizing lotion or cream for dry skin;

- Vaseline (cheaper) or zinc oxide preparation;

- shampoo (optional);

- a pair of small nail scissors;

- for older children: a small, soft-bristled toothbrush and fluoride toothpaste.

Maintain room temperature at between 22°C (72°F) and 24°C (75°F). The bath water must be at body temperature. Do not add bubble bath or similar products. Your baby's skin is sensitive. During the first 2 to 4 weeks, you can use mild soap but not more than 3 times a week and, above all, for soiled areas: it removes the natural protection on your baby's skin and can cause irritation. Make sure that your hands are clean and that your fingernails are short.

Using a washcloth

To ensure that your baby does not get cold, do not undress him right away. First, wash his head and face.

Wash his face with water. Begin by washing around the eyes, starting at the inner corner near the nose, and clean towards the outer corners of the eyes. Use a different corner of the washcloth for each eye. Next, use another corner of a damp washcloth to gently clean outside and behind his ears (avoid pushing the cloth too far into the ear). Do not use cotton swabs since they can damage the eardrum and push wax farther into the ear. Use another corner of the washcloth to clean your baby's nostrils. If your baby's nose is blocked by secretions, it is important to clean it (see "Stuffed nose," page 411).

If need be, wash his head once or twice a week with mild unscented soap or baby shampoo. Do not be afraid to gently rub the baby's soft spot (fontanel). Rinse well with clear water and gently dry.

Carefully wash the folds in your baby's neck. Undress him and remove his diaper. Quickly wash his entire body with a washcloth dipped in lukewarm water, without rubbing. Remember to wash his armpits, thighs and bottom. You may use mild soap but not more than 3 times a week. Be sure to rinse thoroughly. Gently dry your baby

without rubbing and wrap him in a towel to keep him warm.

Bathing your baby in a bathtub

Bathe your baby in a plastic tub, a clean bathroom or kitchen sink, or even in the bathtub with you. **Never leave the baby alone** for any reason, for example, to answer the telephone or the doorbell, not even for a second. A baby can drown in 2.5 to 5 cm (1 to 2 inches) of water.

Put from 8 to 12 cm (3 to 5 inches) of water in the sink or tub, enough to cover your baby up to his shoulders. Spread out a washcloth in the bottom of a plastic tub to prevent your baby from slipping. Undress your baby and remove his diaper. To put the baby in the bathtub, place your arm under his neck to fully support his head, then place your hand under one armpit, as illustrated. Support his bottom and legs with your other hand. Gently slide the baby into the water to avoid frightening him. Soap and rinse him thoroughly and talk to him while you bathe him.

Genital organs

In the case of baby girls, gently clean the vulva by separating the vaginal labial folds. Work from the front to the back to prevent faecal matter from entering the vagina and the urethra. Rinse well. Do not put scented products such as bubble bath or bath oil in the water: they can cause vaginal irritation and urinary infections.

In the case of boys, wash the penis and scrotum. Do not touch the foreskin since it is not loose at birth (see "Genital organs," page 24).

After the bath

Once the baby's bath is finished, wrap him in a dry towel to keep him warm. Dry him quickly and remember to dry the folds in his skin, without rubbing. The use of powder is not recommended since inhalation can cause respiratory problems. If you decide to use baby powder, make such that it does not contain talc. Do not sprinkle the powder directly on the baby's bottom. Put a small amount in your hand and spread it around.

To prevent irritation on the baby's bottom, you can apply a thin layer of Vaseline. If the buttocks are already red and irritated, use a zinc oxide ointment (see "Diaper rash," page 398). These products create a barrier between stools, urine and the skin.

Cutting your baby's fingernails

During your baby's first week of life, his fingernails will be stuck to his skin. It is better not to cut them, since you could injure him.

After several days, the tip of the fingernails detaches itself from the skin. When the nails grow long enough for the baby to scratch himself, you must cut them. Do so after his bath, when the water has softened them, or when he is sleeping. Use a pair of small scissors or nail clippers to clip the toenails straight across. This will prevent them from becoming ingrown. However, the fingernails should be rounded to prevent scratching. Fingernails grow quickly and they must be trimmed regularly.

An important reminder

- Never leave your baby alone on the changing table or in the bath, even for a second.
- If the telephone or doorbell rings, take the time to put your baby in his bed or take him with you. You may decide not to answer the phone.
- Baby seats with suction cups that adhere to the bottom of the bathtub are not recommended. In recent years, too many babies have drowned while using the seats although the parents thought they were safe. They give the impression that the baby is safe, but actually increase the risk of drowning. Nothing can replace parental supervision.
- Why take chances? Change your baby's diaper on the floor to prevent him from falling off the changing table.

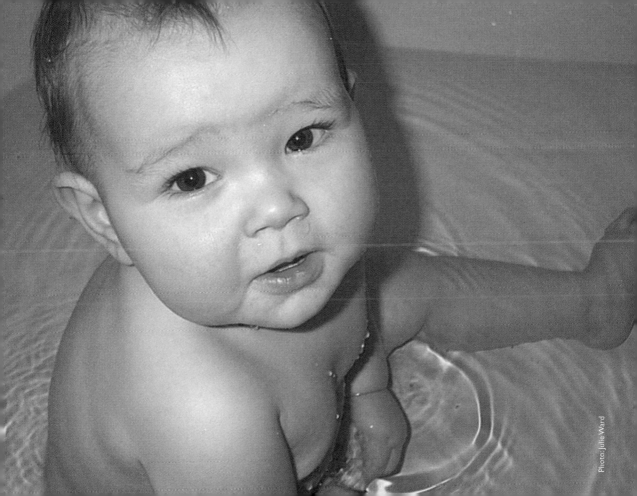

Choice of diapers

Diapers will be part of your baby's wardrobe for approximately 2 ¹/₂ years. Should you buy disposable or cloth diapers? The choice is up to you.

Cloth diapers are less expensive and are ecological. Disposable diapers are more expensive and some babies are allergic to them. However, they are practical. You will perhaps want to buy them occasionally, even if your prefer cotton. If your child is in day care, it is preferable for him to wear paper diapers to minimize the transmission of microbes.

Paper diapers

Paper diapers contain crystals that convert urine into a non-toxic gel and separate it from stools, thus eliminating the urine-stool mixture that is so irritating to baby's skin.

An important reminder

- Some disposable diapers are scented and can cause irritation and allergies.
- Paper diapers often give the impression that the baby is not wet. Check regularly to see whether your baby needs changing.
- Make sure the diaper fasteners do not injure your baby's skin.

Cloth diapers

Ingenious new cloth diapers are easy to use. Simple to adjust, they use Velcro fasteners or snaps and leak-proof gathers. Some models have a removable or semi-removable cushion that facilitates cleaning. Are you looking for an economical solution? Traditional diapers attached with safety pins are still available.

Cloth diapers are less absorbent than paper diapers. Some brands of cloth diapers offer a more absorbent nighttime diaper or an additional absorbent cushion to be inserted in the diaper.

51

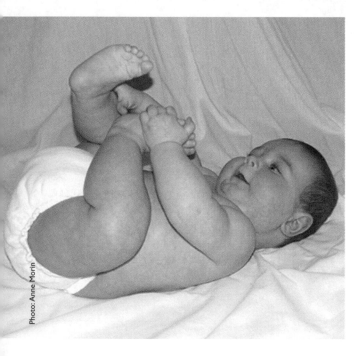

Photo: Anne Morin

Keep your baby dry

You must change your baby as soon as he wets or soils his diaper. Frequent diaper changes will help prevent and soothe irritation. If your baby shows signs of irritation or diaper rash, change his diaper at least once during the night (see "Diaper rash," page 398).

Nylon diaper covers let baby's skin breathe. Plastic pants with elasticized leg openings and waistbands prevent air from circulating, retain moisture and irritate baby's skin. Choose sufficiently large pants. If the elastics leave pronounced marks on the skin, the pants are too small.

Washing diapers

Commercial diaper services are available in some areas, which will make life easier for you. Simply follow the diaper service's recommendations on storing dirty diapers.

If you wash your baby's cotton diapers, **carefully follow the manufacturer's instructions**. Some manufacturers recommend soaking the diapers before washing while others do not.

Cleaning

First discard stools in the toilet. Paper diaper liners make it easier to remove the stools. They are biodegradable and can be flushed down the toilet. If you use a paper diaper, throw it away after emptying it.

Washing

Washing is a very important step. Failure to wash the diapers properly will irritate the baby's skin. To avoid these problems, follow the steps below.

- If the manufacturer recommends soaking the diapers, thoroughly wring them out when you remove them from soaking or spin them in the washing machine.

- Put mild soap in the washing machine and select a warm water wash (or lukewarm water if the diapers are covered with a waterproof coating). Be sure to dissolve the soap before adding the diapers.

- Rinse the diapers in clear water, without fabric softener. Some manufacturers recommend rinsing the diapers twice.

- Thoroughly dry the diapers in a clothes dryer (medium setting), hang them up to dry or dry them in the sun (which helps to whiten them).

53

Do not dry in the dryer certain diapers with a waterproof coating or waterproof diaper covers. Follow the manufacturer's recommendations.

Always wash diapers separately from other clothes. Do not use a detergent designed for delicate fabrics as it will leave a gummy deposit on the diapers. Do not use fabric softeners as they cause irritation and reduce the cloth's absorbency.

Wash and rinse plastic pants often. Wash rubber pants the same way that you wash cloth diapers.

An important reminder

- Wash your baby's bottom and genital organs in lukewarm water every time you change his diaper, whether he is newborn or older.
- To avoid contamination, always wash your hands after changing your baby.
- To prevent irritation, occasionally spread a thin layer of Vaseline or unscented zinc oxide preparation (Ihle's paste, Pâte foufounes, Zincofax or another brand) on your baby's bottom (see "Diaper rash," page 398). Do not overdo it, as the products can make the Velcro fasteners sticky and the diapers less absorbent. The products are also absorbed by the skin.
- Disposable wet towels can also cause irritation and should only be used on healthy skin or when water and soap are unavailable.

Choice of clothing

Your baby's clothes must be soft, comfortable and easy to maintain. There is no point in buying large quantities of clothing of the same size as children grow quickly and their wardrobe must be replaced regularly.

Choose clothing that is not overly fitted. Do not trust the size indicated on the label: even if your baby is only 1 month old, a garment for a 3-month-old infant may be too tight for him. Make sure that the crotch opens easily to change diapers.

You should obviously take into account the ambient temperature when dressing your baby. In summer, a diaper, a light garment or an undershirt are sufficient. Dress your baby a bit more warmly if your home is air conditioned. In winter, pyjamas that cover the baby's feet are ideal in the home. **To determine whether your baby is too hot, touch the nape of his neck: it should not be damp.**

Pyjamas with fitted waists, ankles and wrists are best for sleepwear. They are safer than loose-fitting pyjama tops and bottoms. Make sure that your baby's toes are not curled up in pyjamas that are too short.

Washing your baby's clothes

If your baby has sensitive skin, wash his clothes separately using mild, unscented soap. To completely eliminate all traces of soap, rinse the clothes twice. Poorly rinsed clothes often irritate the skin. It is preferable to wash new garments before using them. Some newborns cannot tolerate fabric softeners.

Your baby's first shoes

Babies usually have flat feet until they are 3 years old. The arch takes shape as the muscles develop. Let your baby walk barefoot in summer about half the time. Walking barefoot is excellent for his feet.

There is no need for shoes before your baby takes his first steps. Only get him shoes when he starts walking. Shoes must be properly adjusted at the heel and be roughly 1.25 cm ($\frac{1}{2}$ inch) longer than your baby's feet. To measure the space between the longest toe and the tip of the shoe, have your baby stand up. You can also measure the inside of the shoe with a measuring tape and compare this measurement with the length of your child's foot (measured while he is standing up).

Shoes should have a semi-rigid sole (the front of the sole should bend under slight pressure). They protect the feet and keep them warm. Ankle boots offer greater support but are not absolutely necessary, although it is harder for your baby to kick them off. Socks must not pinch the toes.

When your child is between 12 and 36 months of age, check the adjustment of his shoes every three months. Buy new shoes frequently. Take your baby to the store so that he can try on the shoes, otherwise you risk getting the wrong size.

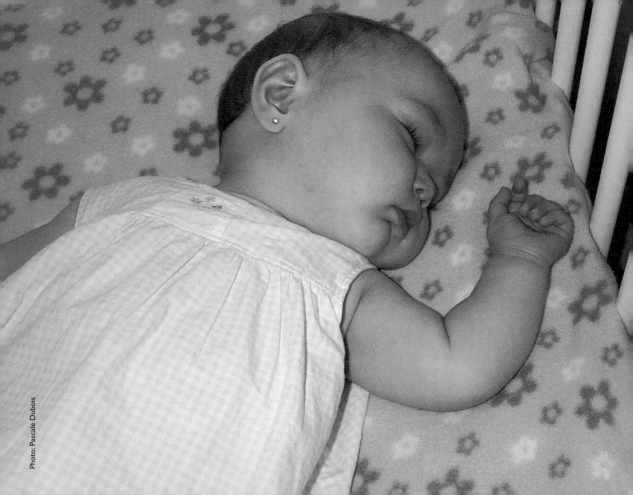

Sleep

Sleeping and waking hours

Newborns sleep for 12 to 17 hours a day. A baby's sleeping and waking hours differ from those of an adult and change as she grows. During the first weeks, your baby will wake up 6 to 8 times every 24 hours, sometimes more often if she is breast-fed, and go back to sleep almost immediately after feeding. She needs to feed often, which wakes her up, even at night. Your baby will not necessarily be hungry when she wakes up. She may simply want to take advantage of your presence.

If your baby has a low birth weight or has lost more than 10% of her weight after birth, you should perhaps wake her up to feed. The same is true of heavy sleepers. In case of doubt, consult a health professional (see "Who can help your baby?" page 314).

After the age of 6 months, a baby's routine stabilizes and she falls asleep more easily. Little by little, you will recognize signs of fatigue and will be able to establish a bedtime routine.

Sleeping through the night

The expression "sleeping through the night" indicates that babies do not have the same waking and sleeping cycles as adults. In other words, babies do not sleep through adults' nights.

Sleeping through the night means sleeping for 5 hours, without interruption, between 11 p.m. and 8 a.m. Newborns very rarely sleep through the night. Some babies sleep through the night at the age of 3 or 4 months. Others do not do so until the age of 6 months, 10 months or more. However, such babies have no trouble sleeping (see "Waking in the night," page 67).

Between the ages of 0 and 6 months, a baby may require a feeding during the night. Do not deprive your baby of this feeding. She may also cry for another reason. You must reassure her.

Some parents find it more practical to keep the baby in their room as long as she needs to feed at night. Others prefer to have the baby sleep in her own room from birth. Adopt the solution that is easiest for you.

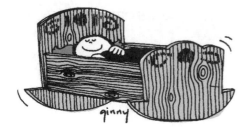

An important reminder

- A premature baby will feed more often than a full-term baby.
- Do not eliminate too quickly the last feeding of the evening. If your baby starts waking up again at night, she may be hungry. Increase the number of feedings or the amount of milk. Do not deprive a baby under 6 months of age of milk when she wakes up at night.
- After 6 months, babies generally feed enough during the day to continue growing at a healthy rate without a night feeding.
- If your baby's nose appears to be blocked by secretions when she wakes up and goes to bed, it is important to clean the secretions accumulated in the nose using a saline solution (see "Stuffed nose," page 411).

Is your baby sleeping enough?

The need for sleep varies from one baby to the next and, generally speaking, each child establishes her own rhythm. Let your baby sleep when she wants to and avoid waking her up, except to feed her. If noise disturbs her, try to adapt your schedule to hers. However, if she sleeps well in a stroller, take advantage of the opportunity to go for brief outings with your baby. She can also, to some extent, adapt to your lifestyle habits.

Crib death

While the sudden death of apparently healthy infants under 1 year of age is inexplicable, it usually occurs while the baby is sleeping. There is greater risk of crib death when:

- the baby is sleeping on her stomach;
- she is too hot;
- the mother smoked during pregnancy or the baby is exposed to smoke.

For reasons that we still do not fully understand, when a baby sleeps in a room separate from her parents, there is a greater risk of crib death.

An important reminder

The risk of crib death increases when the baby sleeps on her stomach and is exposed to cigarette smoke BEFORE or AFTER birth.

Recommended sleeping position

From birth, place your newborn baby **on her back** on a firm mattress. She is not at risk of suffocating on her back. Do not put anything other than a blanket on her bed. Avoid pillows, comforters and other objects designed to immobilize the baby. Even if bumper pads are pretty, health officials advise against them because some babies may bury their faces in the borders.

Flat head

Since paediatricians have recommended that parents place infants on their backs only, crib death cases have fallen by 50% to 70%. However, a word of caution is in order: when a baby always sleeps in the same position, she may suffer from positional plagiocephaly, or flat head. The baby tends to always turn her head to the same side. Since the skull bones are still soft, the part of the head lying on the mattress is flattened. To prevent flat head, the Canadian Paediatric Society recommends changing the baby's position in the crib every day.

- On even-numbered days, place the baby normally in the crib.

- On odd-numbered days, place her in the opposite direction so that her head is at the foot of the crib.

- Encourage your baby to look toward the room, not the wall, by installing, if need be, a mobile on the side of the crib that faces the room (in this way, the position of her head will alternate from one day to the next).

When your baby is awake and someone is watching her, place her on her tummy. Doing so will prevent flat head and foster her development.

After 6 months

Between the ages of 6 and 12 months, your baby, who has been sleeping through the night, may start to wake up. **She may be afraid of losing you when she cannot see you**. If she wakes up, reassure her, speak softly to her and put her back to bed. It may take only your voice and caresses to reassure her. If her crying persists, try to determine its cause. She may be sick. You can take her temperature (see "How to take the temperature," page 404). Does hunger often wake her up? Consider adjusting your baby's daytime feedings.

To help your baby get into the habit of sleeping through the night, it is better not to take her out of the crib. It is important to remember that it is normal for your baby to wake up in the night. She will gradually learn to go back to sleep on her own. Sleeping through the night is a question of temperament, maturity and, occasionally, environment. As their sleeping habits develop, many babies between the ages of 6 and 12 months will sleep from 8 to 10 hours a night and a total of roughly 15 hours a day. A baby who is active during the day, enjoys herself and gets fresh air usually sleeps soundly at night.

Bedtime routine

Little by little, you will recognize when your baby is tired. Plan her bedtime routine so that it is pleasant for her and for you. Repeating the same gestures every night creates a bedtime routine that prepares your child for soothing sleep.

The conditions in which a baby goes to sleep are the same ones she needs to go back to sleep at night. If she needs your presence to go to sleep then she will likely need it to go back to sleep after awakening at night. However, you can help your baby to learn to go back to sleep on her own and thus develop her autonomy during the night.

Avoid games that overexcite the baby. Help her calm down by giving her a bath. Then, provide her blanket, favourite toy and **the warmth of her father or mother rocking her.** Play **soft music** or sing her a song. When she is older, tell her a story. You can leave a night light on in the hall and the door of the baby's room ajar.

To go back to sleep after partly awakening, a child needs the same conditions as those prevailing when she goes to sleep. If she goes to sleep in her father's or her mother's arms, she will need her parents arms to go back to sleep. A transitional object that the child keeps with her and can pick up when she reawakens is important to create the conditions that help her to fall asleep.

When you leave your baby's room, never do so suddenly. Tell your baby that you are leaving and when you will return. Even small children understand.

A child's sleep, like that of an adult, has several phases that are repeated during the night according to a variable cycle (partial reawakening may occur between each cycle). One phase is rapid eye movement (REM) sleep. During this phase, your baby's eyes move under her eyelids, she dreams and sometimes has nightmares.

Nightmares and night terrors

It is nighttime and your baby starts to cry. However, she appears to be sleeping deeply. Your attempts to console her seem ineffective. Do not worry, she will soon calm down. Do not intervene unless you fear that she will injure herself in her agitated state. Your baby is experiencing night terrors, as a number of children do beyond the age of 1 year.

If she awakens in a state of panic and seems to be fully awake, she has undoubtedly had a nightmare. Your baby may have trouble getting back to sleep. Console her promptly and reassure her. Do not worry, nightmares or night terrors usually disappear as the child ages. Several books give tips on teaching children how to deal with these situations. Consult the suggested reading list at the back of this guide.

Between 1 and 2 years

Children between 1 and 2 years of age sleep from 8 to 12 hours a night. Until the age of 18 months, children usually need to take 2 naps, in the morning and the afternoon. Between the ages of 18 months and 2 years, they may need only 1 nap. Your baby may be cranky when she wakes up. Be patient and wait a few minutes before resuming activities. The need for sleep varies from one baby to the next and generally diminishes with age.

Bedtime problems

Many children between 1 and 2 years of age cry at bedtime. They need to be reassured. If this is the case with your child, be patient but firm. Explain clearly that the day is over and it is time to sleep. Leave her bedroom once you have reassured her. Establishing a bedtime routine will help your baby to fall asleep.

If she cries, wait for 5 minutes, then return to say "good night" softly for 30 seconds. Leave the room again. If she cries again, repeat the same procedure every 5 minutes at first, then lengthen the interval until she falls asleep. One week of this routine is usually all it takes.

Waking in the night

If your child wakes up crying during the night and calls you, go to her immediately. See what is bothering her, take care of her, console her and put her back to bed. Unless your baby is sick, do not linger with her. If she is thirsty, only give her water since milk and juice can cause cavities.

If your child wakes up persistently, too frequently (more than twice a night), for periods of over 20 minutes, requires the presence of a parent, wakes up more than 4 or 5 nights out of 7, or has been waking up at night for at least 3 months, consult the suggested reading list or talk to a health professional.

To promote sleep

- Your baby should learn to fall asleep by herself in her own bed. She may need your help in learning how to do so, just as she needs you to learn to walk and develop good eating habits.

- Although the mother and father may interact differently with the baby, both parents must agree on the bedtime routine and maintain it.

- Avoid watching television before bedtime as children's programs are stimulating and do not promote sleep.

- Avoid lively, noisy discussions in front of your baby, especially if she is crying.

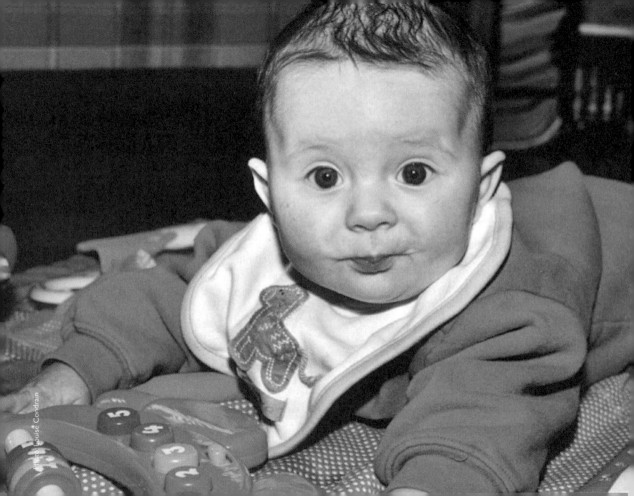

Your Child's Development

A child's growth is an ongoing and wonderful process. To develop harmoniously, your child needs love, tenderness and play just as much as food, care, sleep and physical safety and emotional security. By ensuring that you satisfy all of your baby's essential needs, you will gradually rediscover the magic of childhood.

Your child wants to be:

- **accepted** as he is – your love and understanding will help him develop his personality;

- **supported** – your encouragement will help develop his skills and self-confidence;

- **stimulated** – an adapted environment will enable him to enjoy enriching experiences with the objects and people around him;

- **guided** in his experience – proper, constant, clear limits will help prepare him to experience positive interaction with his peers when he enters day care, integrate successfully into his school, and behave appropriately later in life at work and in society.

From the start of pregnancy, parents begin to develop affection for their child. Your child's affection for each of you will develop through the daily care you give him.

The importance of bonding

Affection is a human trait and is the bond that develops between an infant and the adults, usually his parents, who take care of him. This bond will last for a lifetime, although it is expressed differently depending on your child's growing autonomy.

Most parents, regardless of their age, level of education or culture, are sensitive to the fragile appearance of their newborn. Their desire to protect the child and awareness of his dependency encourage them to promptly respond to his crying. These are the ways that babies ask for their parents when they need to be fed, changed, consoled and reassured.

In his first year of life, your baby displays his attachment by seeking your presence. A child seeks this contact with his parents especially when he is afraid and distressed. Contact with and the presence of his parents reassures him. When your baby becomes calm he is once again prepared to explore his environment.

A child's development alters the expression of his affectionate behaviour. He gradually learns to tolerate delays, he can say what he wants, and he can talk about his emotions and intentions. A child learns to interact and communicate through his affection for his parents. Later, he will learn to understand their point of view and develop the ability to agree with them on joint projects.

The parent plays a key role in offering his child a basic sense of security and is the ideal person to satisfy the child's emotional needs. Separation is likely to make the child protest. When his parents come back, the child may express his displeasure or discomfort resulting from their absence and his joy and pleasure at seeing them again. Once contact has been re-established, a child whose affection has been secured becomes curious about his environment. To satisfy his need for exploration, with his parents' encouragement, he will turn to new centres of interest.

Solid bonding instils in your baby a feeling of trust, safety and well-being that will affect his personality and help him to develop a stronger, more independent personality. These qualities foster his relations with other people.

Later in life, they will allow him to become an attentive, loving parent.

Temperament

Every baby is born with his own traits, which are more readily apparent after the age of 4 months. Is your baby easygoing? Sensitive? Cautious? Each newborn is unique.

Some babies are easygoing and sleep peacefully. They wake up and feed according to a regular schedule. They are usually good-humoured and moderately active. They adapt readily to change and it is relatively easy to satisfy their needs.

Other babies are more sensitive. Their schedule is not regular and their demands vary from one day to the next. They adapt less readily to change and sometimes cry intensely. They may be irritable and colicky. **Parents discover that these children, while they demand flexibility, also need clearly defined limits. Children need stable, reliable guidelines** (see "The need for supervision and discipline," page 79). **To help these children, parents make adjustments by offering greater regularity in the schedules proposed**.

Some babies are more cautious. They are less excitable, move less and take time to observe before they act. They are more timid, slower and more resistant to change when new activities occur. Since they are often quieter and demand less attention, they may seem more independent. **It is good to encourage them, bearing in mind their pace in order to help them discover new things**. Even if they reflect and take their time, they understand as much as other children and learn to explore, socialize and play with other children just like livelier, quicker babies.

This perception of a child's temperament is not rigid and some parents also report that their baby has a "mixed" temperament that combines all 3 categories.

Take the time to observe your child in order to discover his traits and need for encouragement and supervision. These observations are important since they will guide your approach and educational initiatives. To foster harmonious development, we encourage parents to adjust their behaviour to their child's temperament. In this way, the child will feel understood and that his parents respect his pace.

To interact is to stimulate

A baby needs frequent, appropriate contact with his surroundings, especially his parents. From birth, your baby has everything he needs to interact: eyesight, hearing and touch. As he grows, his abilities will improve.

Through care and playing, which foster interaction, you can stimulate the development of your child's abilities. A harmonious exchange occurs during moments of interaction that allow your baby to get to know you and to learn to anticipate. From the age of 6 months, he finds in you an intermediary who puts him into contact with objects and the environment. You introduce him to the world.

Your baby understands language several months before he knows how to speak. Talk to him, describe what you are doing and your gestures: "Look, mommy is going to feed you," or "Daddy is giving you a bath," and so on. Do not be afraid to repeat yourself as your child is registering what you say.

Playing: your child's first school

Playing is an essential activity for your child's development. Through play he expresses his joy at being alive and discovers his body, his family and his home.

Playing is a child's first learning experience. During the first 2 years of life, he will make great strides. He will learn to:

- crawl, walk, climb, run and dance (overall motor skills);

- use his hands and fingers to hold and manipulate objects and coordinate eye and hand movements (fine motor skills);

- understand language and talk;

- develop his intelligence;

- discover the world around him and his place in it;

- take pride in his successes and develop self-confidence.

All children love playing for 2 good reasons: it is amusing and instructive. Through playing, a child discovers the world, uses his newfound skills and learns to analyse the environment.

Choice of toys

Choose safe toys that satisfy your child's needs (see "Toys and safety," page 366).

It is important to give your child stimulating toys. It is better to give him a toy dog on wheels that he can push or pull than a battery-operated dog that he only looks at, and to take the time to play with him. Help your baby discover his new toys. The experience he shares with his mother and father will always be worth more than the most sophisticated toy, especially if it is forgotten at the back of the closet.

The most expensive toys are not the best ones. Your child can have fun playing with common household items such as saucepans, plastic utensils, bowls and, of course, cardboard boxes, which can be turned into houses, tunnels, cars and hats.

Instead of overloading the toy box, rediscover the joys of childhood with your baby. Interaction with your baby will stimulate his development and yours. Take time to play with your baby and cajole him. You will discover the pleasure of being together.

🔲 **Handy hint**

After very active playing or before your child's bedtime, choose calmer activities. Read your child a story, rock his teddy bear to encourage him to go to sleep, or sing a gentle song.

Frequently asked questions on language

Communication with your child starts at birth and is a key facet of his development. Children acquire language gradually (see "Stages in your baby's development," page 86), which enables them to express themselves and establish contact with the people around them.

Language learning can become a source of concern for parents. Before you worry, remember that not all children develop at the same pace. Some children start talking early on, while others only begin later. Temperaments also differ: some children are quiet while others are talkative.

Here are answers to some of the questions on language that parents ask most frequently.

How should I talk to my child?

Use simple words and short sentences. Speak slowly and repeat yourself often. Your baby will certainly use words like "baba" for bottle, "dok" for dog or "coe" for comb. Set a good example. When your baby says "walu," answer, "Oh yes, **water**." As he grows, you will naturally adapt to his level.

What should I do if my child does not speak?

It is important to avoid pressuring your child and to keep exchanges pleasant. Develop a strategy to encourage him to express himself.

- Create amusing situations to arouse his interest. For example, try to put his boots on your big feet or pretend to fall asleep when you are playing with him.

- Do not go beyond his needs. Pretend to forget his spoon. He will have to attempt to express himself in order to ask for it.

- Ask your baby open questions that require a response other than "yes" or "no," for example: "What do you want to eat?"

- Offer him choices: "Do you want an apple or an orange?"

- Say only the beginning of words: "Do you want a ba... (banana)?"

- Encourage all of his efforts to use new words and praise him when he does.

What should I do if I cannot understand my child?

Without blaming your child, indicate to him that you did not understand what he said: "Sorry, I wasn't paying attention." Encourage all of his attempts to communicate even if you do not understand him. If you understand a few words, try to guess what he is saying by speculating: "Something happened to your teddy bear?" If you have no idea what he is trying to say, ask him to show you what he is talking about.

What should I do if my child mispronounces words?

Some sounds are harder to master than others and will appear later in your child's language. For example, children up to the age of 5 or 6 years of age may distort "s" as in **s**un, "z" as in **z**oo, "sh" as in **sh**oe, "j" as in **j**ump, "ch" as in **ch**eese, "v" as in **v**ery, "th" as in **th**ing, and "th" as in **th**at. To help your child master sounds, repeat the words correctly and emphasize the incorrectly produced sound. **Do not demand that your child repeat the word**. Maintain pleasant communication by avoiding constant repetitions. Focus on what your child is saying, not how he says it.

When should I consult a health professional?

To speak correctly, your child must hear properly. If you are concerned about his hearing, consult your doctor, who may refer your child for an audiogram.

Consult a health professional in the following instances.

Around 6 months: Your baby does not react to your voice or ambient sounds and rarely babbles.

Around 12 months: Your child stops making sounds and makes no gestures when he wants to communicate. He does not react to familiar words such as his name, the names of important people around him, his teddy bears and favourite toys.

Around 18 months: He does not use any words and does not understand familiar, simple instructions.

Around 24 months: He does not combine 2 or more words and mostly expresses himself through gestures.

Around 3 years: Strangers cannot understand your child, who does not speak in sentences or take the initiative to communicate. He does not understand simple sentences.

Should you see a speech-language pathologist?

Language is essential to your child's development and to communication. Once your child goes to school, he will have to express himself and make himself understood. If you suspect that your child is lagging or notice specific problems, have him examined by a speech-language pathologist.

The Ordre des orthophonistes et des audiologistes du Québec has a directory of speech-language pathologists and audiologists in your area (see "Useful addresses," page 441).

The need for supervision and discipline

Parents have their own ideas about education, which they have probably inherited from their own parents and adapted to the times. Some parents are permissive, while others are strict. Regardless of your approach, what is most important is to trust your judgment as an individual and respect your child, bearing in mind his needs, temperament and age.

However, just as your infant needs care that will enable him to develop physically and emotionally, he also requires supervision and discipline.

Clear rules

To love a child also means imposing certain limits, which are necessary to prevent him from harming himself, and teaching him to respect others and the environment. Your child thus needs rules, but since he does not yet know them, you must teach him.

This process usually begins once the child is able to move about easily, around the age of 9 months. At that age, your baby is able to learn simple rules and understand when you forbid him to do something.

Learn to say **NO**

Suppose that your child wants to touch the oven door and you have just told him not to. Say NO firmly. You can then move him away and offer him a toy to distract him. If he starts to play, congratulate him. If he cries, repeat NO softly and be sure to reassure him. If he comes back to the oven, repeat the process.

Importance of the emotional bond

The solidity of the emotional bond that you establish with your child at birth will make it much easier for you to impose limits on him when the time comes. A child who feels loved, understood and respected will be much more willing to accept guidance than a child who does not feel valued.

Develop patience

When your child is between 9 and 12 months old, you can start to teach him that he can wait for a few minutes before his needs are satisfied. It is important to be reassuring during these initial waiting periods. Continue to talk to him or give him a toy. In this way, he will have an opportunity to gradually develop his patience in different situations of everyday life, such as meal preparation, attention given to another child or an important telephone call.

Need for discipline

Discipline ensures, first and foremost, an infant's physical and emotional well-being. It also facilitates life in society, now and in the future. To ensure that discipline is effective, parents must decide together what is permissible. In this way, they can set clear rules for their child without contradicting themselves.

Physical well-being: Parents must prevent behaviour that is likely to injure the child. For example, prevent him from climbing on an unstable object. To avoid the tiresome repetition of rules forbidding him to do something, organize the house in a safe manner.

Emotional well-being: Children need routines because they like things to be repeated in more or less the same order, which allows them to anticipate and place themselves in relation to events. Your child will be reassured if meals, bedtime or the departure time for day care occur in a foreseeable order.

Hygiene and public-spiritedness: In the same way that you teach your infant to eat with a spoon, put objects in a tub or use the potty, you will teach him some basic rules of life that, later on, will foster his social integration:

- wash his hands before meals;
- brush his teeth in the morning and at night;
- say "please" and "thank you";
- avoid speaking at the same time as someone else;
- wait for his turn, and so on.

To facilitate discipline

- At mealtimes, it will be easier to maintain discipline if you always seat your child in his highchair.

- Bedtime will be less painful if you establish early on in your child's life a bedtime routine and stick to it.

- Teach your child one rule at a time, starting with the ones that are the most important to you. Introduce a new rule ONLY when the preceding one has been fully integrated into everyday life: tiny tots can only retain a few instructions at a time. You must take into account his age and ability to understand what you are asking him, and even to remember it.

- From the age of 18 months or 2 years, you can take time to explain to your child the reasons for a rule. If your explanation is simple, clear and colourful and you show him exactly what you expect of him, it will be easier for your child to understand, accept and even adopt the rule.

- Games can be a very useful tool for teaching children certain elements of discipline. For example, toddlers are very fond of being with their parents and imitating what they are doing. Having your child act like a grownup can be a way of teaching him to pick up his toys or clothing.

How to react to a lack of discipline

If your child refuses to obey a rule that you have taken the time to explain to him, you must be firm. Firmness is apparent on your face and in your tone of voice. Never strike your child, since he will learn fear, disrespect and aggressiveness, and will strike others in turn to obtain what he wants, according to the model he has learned. There are more effective ways to counteract a child's refusal.

Isolate the child: Most day care centres use this method, which you might find useful. Place a small chair in a quiet place somewhat removed from toys and household activities. When your child refuses to obey a request or instruction, take him by the hand and accompany him to the chair and have him sit there briefly. Two or three minutes will suffice, since he will forget why he is sitting there if kept there too long. Initially, your child may not stay seated. Without saying anything, every time he gets up without your permission, lead him back to the chair and have him sit down once again. If your child is very determined, you will have to be just as determined. You must teach him the rules you deem to be important and he must learn to obey them. After all, you are the parent. Once you allow your child to leave the chair, explain the rule to him again and thank him for his understanding.

Be firm: Some children need more supervision than others. As parents, you are in the best position to assess your tiny tot's needs and traits. When the rule imposed is necessary or, indeed, essential to your child's well-being, for example, bedtime, do not hesitate to maintain your demands. Be perseverant. However, avoid constantly repeating an instruction without doing anything to ensure compliance with it, since your child will deduce that obedience is not necessary.

Discipline without discouraging

Good discipline means spending more time and energy encouraging your child than reprimanding him. Trying to steer your child toward acceptable behaviour gives better results than constantly criticizing him for what he does wrong. A child who is bombarded with instructions or reprimanded too often risks becoming upset or discouraged.

Do not hesitate to congratulate your child when he does something right. As you teach him what you expect of him, your encouragement will reassure him about his abilities and skills. It is through his daily experience that your child builds self-esteem and develops a positive idea of his individual worth. Joys and successes, as much as difficulties and frustrations, will teach your child about life.

The challenge facing parents is to strike a balance in their disciplinary relationship with the child.

It is just as important to encourage desirable behaviour as it is to correct undesirable behaviour.

The Terrible 2s

During the period known as the Terrible 2s, between the ages of 18 months and 3 years, the child feels an urgent need to oppose all requests. In fact, the child is experiencing his first assertiveness crisis. He is testing what he knows and is also learning. Gradually, he will understand that some things are not permitted, that our gestures have consequences, that there are limits and rules to be obeyed in society. This is a crucial time for both the child and his parents to experience discipline. It is a trying period.

Let us take a well-known example, a crying fit in the supermarket. Your little angel throws a tantrum because you refuse to buy him candy. He shouts his head off, screams and kicks. He may even hurt you or roll on the ground.

Obviously, everyone is watching you, some shoppers compassionately, others accusingly. What should you do?

The offside tactic: Remove the child from the situation. Leave your shopping cart and take the child outside the store. Once you are well away from spectators, calmly but firmly explain to your child that you will not go back into the store until he understands your refusal. This radical change of situation should surprise your child and have the desired effect. Wait for him to calm down before resuming your shopping. You will perhaps have the impression that this exercise is a waste of time, but the limits that you establish in this way are essential and will save you time later on.

This process consists essentially in withdrawing a child from a difficult situation for several minutes to explain to him what you expect of him. It is preferable to punishment, which often fails to explain to the child why he is being criticized or what is expected of him.

Worthwhile efforts

The first confrontations are trying. It is important for both parents to work together to establish healthy discipline. The daily effort you will have to make is, in fact, an investment in the future. Love, respect, flexibility, patience and perseverance are necessary qualities in parents who wish to play their role as educators. By gradually educating your child to the rules of family and social life, you will enable him to develop self-discipline later in life.

A number of reference books on discipline are available from libraries or bookstores.

Stages in your baby's development

Here are some pointers that will help you traverse the great adventure of motherhood and fatherhood and monitor your child's development, along with ideas for activities that are amusing for parents and children alike.

It should be noted that the ages indicated are intended to serve as a guideline only. Each child develops at his own pace and may acquire new skills sooner or later than anticipated.

The age of premature babies

If your baby was born prematurely, his age must be adjusted. Your pre-term child will need to take the time to experience the weeks of maturing that he missed in his mother's womb. This catching up will not occur through the magic of birth. It will take place slowly over the years, up to the age of 5. When you make comparisons with growth curves, stages of development or other children, you should use the **adjusted age**; otherwise your expectations may be too high. Consult the Association des parents d'enfants prématurés (see "Useful addresses," page 442).

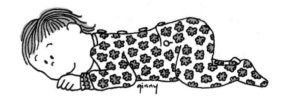

An important reminder

To adjust the age of a pre-term baby, simply calculate his age based on his anticipated date of birth. For example, if you gave birth on January 1, at the seventh month of pregnancy, your baby's real age will be 3 months on April 1. However, since you should have given birth on March 1, his adjusted age will be only 1 month, as though he were a full-term baby.

Up to 2 months

During his first weeks of life, your baby will move a lot. His movements are unorganized and involuntary. Do not worry, this is normal. Your baby is at the reflex stage.

Is he startled by louder noises or quick movements? Contrary to what some parents think, such reactions are not a sign of excessive nervousness, but the **Moro's reflex**.

The **sucking reflex** is fully developed and allows your child to eat or calm himself by putting his fist in his mouth. A derivative of this reflex will make him turn his head if you tickle his cheek or arm. It will also enable him to seek the breast.

When he is supported under the arms and held upright, a newborn will take a few steps on the examining table (the doctor can show you): the **stepping reflex**. Of course, your baby cannot bear his own weight.

At birth, your child has extraordinary abilities that you can perceive by watching him. What is exciting is that he amuses himself every day by doing new things. He is not too small to play.

His senses are awakening. Touch the palm of his hand and he will try to grab your finger. Hang a mobile over his crib and he will look at it. Soon, he will follow with his eyes a moving object. Shake his rattle and he will react to the noise. His memory is also developing. He recognizes your voice and likes to hear it. He looks for your face and discovers you. He is already communicating in his own way!

Activities up to 2 months

Decorate the wall – Put photographs on the walls and coloured cards or a children's book that your baby can look at while you change his diaper. Replace them often as this will revive his interest.

Talk to your child – Look at your child when you are holding him. You will get to know each other better. Speak softly to him, tell him a story or sing him a song. Imitate the noises he makes and wait for his reaction. In this way, you will encourage him to pronounce sounds, help him learn rhythms and intonations, and make him want to participate in the conversation. Say his name often and soon he will recognize it. Move about when you call him and he will move his head in the direction of the sounds he hears. Do not be afraid to repeat yourself as this is essential for language learning.

2 to 3 months

Your baby holds his head up more easily and becomes more active. When lying on his stomach, he is able to prop himself up on his forearms and gradually raise his upper body. He moves his legs and explores his feet and hands. He likes it when you play with his hands, move his legs in a pedalling motion and pretend to eat his tummy.

He grabs a rattle and puts it in his mouth to suck on it. Do not be surprised. For a time, he will put everything in his mouth. That is how he learns. He will play with his tongue and saliva, and blow bubbles.

He reacts to the voices of familiar people and noise-making toys. He does not yet understand words but likes it when you sing, since he recognizes your voice and feels secure. He pays attention to the melody and to gestures. Is he crying? Speak softly to him and perhaps he will calm down.

He can focus his attention to listen to music. He is interested in the human face and will smile when smiled at. From the age of 3 months, he becomes increasingly aware of the presence of other family members.

Activities, 2 to 3 months

A tour of the house – Take your baby on a guided tour of the house. Show him objects and name them. He will try to grab them. In this way, he can develop his hand-eye coordination.

Tickling – When baby is taking his bath or while playing, introduce him to textures. Tickle him with a toothbrush, a tissue, a teddy bear, a dry washcloth, a plastic toy, and so on.

4 to 5 months

Your baby holds himself up more easily as he is growing stronger. His weight has probably doubled since birth (see "How baby grows," page 317). When lying on his back, he raises his head, puts his feet in his mouth and pedals in the air. If you hold his hands, he gets up on his feet and his head follows the motion. His back is straight but still needs to be supported. When he is on his tummy, he sometimes rolls over on his back and thinks it is great fun. He babbles "papa, gaga, mama, tata." He looks at his hands, puts

them in his mouth, grasps objects easily, holds them properly, then drops them but does not look for them.

He likes to have big colourful objects suspended within his reach and enjoys looking at them, touching them and turning them. He can follow an object with his eyes but may go cross-eyed. His eyesight is very good and he can make out small details. He also recognizes his family. This is the time to check to see if he:

- reacts to your smile;
- stops crying when you talk to him;
- turns toward you when you say his name;
- follows you with his eyes without constantly going cross-eyed.

If your baby reacts very little and you are concerned, talk to your doctor.

Now that your baby is more alert, he more actively seeks your company. He may cry because he is bored and wants someone to move him around and coo. He may even interrupt nursing to look at his father and mother. Keep him with you and talk to him. Pick your baby up as often as you like, even when he is not crying.

At this age, your child takes an interest in the people around him. He attempts to locate the source of noises. He expresses his needs through cries, crying and babbling. He explores his voice, tries

out sounds, repeats them and tries to imitate the sounds you make. Talk to him often. When he babbles, answer him.

Activities, 4 to 5 months

Lying on his tummy – Put your child on his tummy and place safe but interesting objects in front of him. This will encourage him to stretch his arms and grab and handle the objects. He will thus learn to coordinate his movements and learn about shapes and textures. Remember to congratulate him on his efforts.

Peek-a-boo – Cover and uncover your face several times with your hands and say "peek-a-boo." Start the game again with his favourite toy: he will be surprised and pleased to see it reappear so quickly. At this age, children believe that the people or objects they can no longer see have really vanished.

6 to 7 months

Your baby begins to crawl around and moves more quickly and skilfully. When he is lying on his tummy, he props himself up on his hands with his arms straight. You can encourage him to move forward by holding out a small ball or a teddy bear. He can grasp smaller objects.

ginny

He understands his name. He catches certain familiar words such as "daddy" and "teddy bear." He still likes to imitate the sounds you make.

He is starting to eat solid food. During meals, he must remain close to you, seated and properly strapped into his highchair. He likes to play with bowls and bits of food. While nursing, he holds the breast with both hands. He will sometimes turn, with the nipple in his mouth, to follow activities around him. He is starting to teethe and will probably discover the pleasure of biting.

He likes mirrors and objects that he can handle, turn and move. He particularly likes big plastic blocks. Noise-making toys fascinate him: he will bang objects together or on the edge of the table. He adores toys that are squeezed and make a noise. He never tires of repeating the same games. Your baby does not throw things on the floor to oblige you to pick them up and annoy you. He is experimenting, learning to throw objects and watch them fall.

Your baby discovers his body and his parents' faces. He needs to touch his parents, put his fingers in their mouths, noses and eyes. He clings to their clothing. He likes grimaces that make him laugh and learns to tease.

Your child learns through your activities with him. He accumulates knowledge and puts it into practice.

Activities, 6 to 7 months

The parts of the body – Identify the parts of your face and your baby's face, then name the parts of the body.

Mirror, mirror on the wall – Sit or stand in front of a mirror with your baby. Make funny faces and smile. Your baby will learn to recognize himself and recognize you. Make noises with your mouth. Your baby will try to answer you by repeating them.

Discover the world – Take your baby outside, summer and winter. Doing so is good for your health and for your baby's health. Show him the world around him: trees, birds, flowers, and other children, in the park and elsewhere.

8 to 9 months

Your baby crawls faster and tries to stand up by holding onto furniture or grabbing his parents' clothing. Let him move around. He needs to do so in order to get to know his environment. Eye and hand movements are now better coordinated. Your baby drinks by himself at the table. He can pick up tiny objects such as crumbs, which he holds between his thumb and forefinger. He understands certain words ("daddy" or "teddy bear") placed in short sentences ("Where is daddy?" or "Do you want your teddy bear?"). He readily understands gestures in familiar situations. If you ask him for his teddy bear by holding out your hand, he can give it to you.

He can become anxious. He does not like to be separated from the person who is mainly responsible for looking after him and cries when the person leaves. Play "peek-a-boo" with him: he will understand that you do not disappear permanently when you leave him and will learn to keep a mental picture of you.

Avoid changing babysitters and leaving your baby with people he does not know. After you have left or when he wakes up, your absence may make him anxious. At all times and especially if he has to take a nap, explain to him that you are leaving and that you will come back soon. If possible, plan your return to work if you are on maternity leave prior to or after this period in your baby's life. To compensate for his parents' absence, a baby may become attached to substitute objects such as a blanket or rag doll, on which he chews. Take good care of the object and wash it when baby is sleeping. If possible, have on hand 2 identical objects. During washing, one can replace the other.

You will notice that your baby enjoys looking at his blocks, teddy bear and bowl from every possible angle: he is learning about perspective. When looking at himself in a mirror, he tries to catch his reflection and yours. He observes himself. Say his name, which he has understood for some time, and tell him that he is seeing himself.

Activities, 8 to 9 months

The tunnel – Make a tunnel out of a big cardboard box opened at both ends for your baby to crawl through. Be sure to remove any staples. Get down on your hands and knees and play with him: you will see how your baby perceives the world.

Blocks, balls and bottles – Give your baby blocks to stack up, balls to push and floating toys for his bath. He loves filling and emptying plastic bottles and small containers. Avoid rubber objects that hold water since they harbour microbes.

Books and words – Read stories to your baby to help him learn new words. Choose books with simple, colourful pictures.

10 to 11 months

Your baby wants to explore the whole house. He moves very quickly on all fours and can escape your watchful eye in a twinkling (see "Be careful," page 370). He becomes more and more independent. If he is not yet walking, he can stand by himself. He uses furniture to help him stand up, takes a step or two, then falls and starts all over again.

He understands what you say, especially if you speak clearly and simply. He says "ta ta" and "bye bye," plays peek-a-boo and laughs heartily. He becomes very sociable and communicates in order to obtain something or attract attention. It becomes easier to understand him because he accompanies his babbling with gestures: when he says "ba ba" he points to the desired object.

Your baby is afraid of strangers, except when he is in your arms. His parents are still his centre of interest, but he explores his environment with a great deal of curiosity. He can try your patience. However, bear in mind that his curiosity is a sign of sound development.

Your baby enjoys imitating you and pretends to feed his teddy bear or put it to sleep. He may display a preference for a cloth animal or a doll.

He starts to take an interest in books and music. His dexterity improves: he can transfer objects from one hand to the other and loves to fill up and empty containers. He may begin to play by himself but prefers it when daddy horses around with him.

Activities, 10 to 11 months

A ball – Sit on the floor facing your baby with your legs apart. Roll the ball between your baby's legs. Ask him to roll it back. Display your pleasure when he succeeds, he will be very proud of himself.

A toy box – Put a toy box within reach containing simple, colourful, washable toys such as balls, plastic blocks, stacking rings, and cotton animals. Your baby will start to play by himself.

Follow Baby Pluto...

He's hot on the trail of learning fun for your baby!

3 FREE
Baby's First DISNEP
BOOKS and a
FREE BONUS GIFT!

See inside

Baby's First Disney Books

make discovering the world almost as much fun as play

"Learning" seems like such a big concept when talking about little babies. But it's actually easy and fun – almost like playtime – when you do it with Baby's First Disney Books!

Here are the same friendly Disney characters you grew up with... but presented as adorable little babies – just about the same age as your own baby. What fun yo child will have learning about shapes by building a snowfriend with Baby Donald... learning colours with Winnie the Pooh... or finding out about opposites with Simba and Nala. Other early lessons include letters, colours, counting, matching and more

Sturdy board pages... colourful pictures... and lots and lots of fun!

Every book is made of heavy-duty "board" pages that really stand up to lots of us Plus, they're filled with bright, colourful pictures of everyday objects your baby can recognize: shoes... flowers... blocks... balls... stuffed animals and more. So because your own baby is busy seeing and doing the same things as Disney characters in the stories, your child will turn to these books again and again for lots of learning fu

Send for your 3 FREE BOOKS today!

6" x 7" size is ideal
for baby's tiny hands.

Plus the sturdy "board" pages
and rounded edges mean no
sharp corners!

The learning fun starts with
3 FREE BOOKS plus a FREE TOTE BAG!

Introductory Special!
Trial Book only $1.99*!

Yellow and Yummy

Pooh
A BOOK ABOUT COLORS

Lovable Disney characters introduce your baby to learning fun!

Send for 4 FREE GIFTS today!

FREE!
Bonus Gift!

Baby's First DISNEY BOOKS

YES! I want my baby to discover the fun of Baby's First Disney Books! Send my 3 FREE Board Books, plus the colourful Tote bag. Also send a fourth book, Yellow and Yummy, for a seven-day free trial.

If not 100% satisfied with the trial book, I'll return it — at your expense — and owe Grolier nothing. When I keep the book, I'll pay the special introductory price of just $1.99*. Then, about once a month, I'll receive three new books, on seven-day approval of course, at the everyday low price of $5.49* per book.

I may examine the books for seven days and return any book in the program at your expense. After accepting as few as three shipments of three books each, I may cancel at any time by following the instructions on the invoice.

By joining, each year I'll also receive, on approval, a special Disney Yearbook and a Disney Calendar as they are published. I will be notified prior to each shipment of details and the then-current price. I may cancel any shipment I do not wish to receive.

All my child's FREE GIFTS are ours to keep no mather what!

* With membership. Plus shipping, handling and applicable sales tax. All orders subject to approval. Book titles subject to change.

(PLEASE PRINT)   44735 342X-9

		M / D / Y
Child's full name	☐ Boy ☐ Girl	Birthdate

☐ MR.
☐ MS.
☐ MRS.   **Your** first name   Last name

Address   Apt.   P.O. Box

City   Province   Postal code

(   )
Telephone   E-mail (if you would like to receive communications from Grolier by email)

X
Signature (by signing, I declare that I have reached the age of 18)   From Tiny Tot to Toddler

☐ Cochez ici pour la version française. (Le choix et le prix peuvent être différents.)

☐ Have you bought anything by mail in the last:
☐ 6 months ☐ Year ☐ Never

 Printed in Canada
© 2004 Grolier Inc. © Disney

We respect your privacy.
Our privacy statement will be included in your first shipment.

CMA Member

A kitchen cupboard for baby – Give your baby permission to explore a kitchen cupboard well away from the stove filled with plastic plates of different shapes. While your baby plays, you can peacefully prepare a meal. Remember to close the other cupboards with safety latches.

Smells – During meals, introduce your baby to different smells: bread, meat, fruits, vegetables and spices. He will develop his sense of smell.

Books – Give your baby his first stiff cardboard or cloth books. He will learn to identify the objects illustrated in them and later on to name them.

12 to 13 months

Your baby now weighs 3 times as much as he did at birth (see "How baby grows," page 317). He is walking, or almost. However, there is no hurry as each baby develops at his own pace. Perhaps your baby will walk when he is 15 or 18 months old. Do not force him. Soon he will climb on chairs and footstools or will have fun pushing them around. He will delight in climbing stairs. Be especially vigilant.

Your baby discovers shapes. He puts small cubes into bigger ones, balls into holes and rings on a cone. He arranges objects by shape and colour.

He usually says his first words around the age of 12 months. He says "mamma" and "dada" and can say a few words like "down," "wait" and "more." He understands several words. He likes to repeat what he hears. He will soon be able to use 20 or so words, which are still not clear. He still talks gibberish.

Activities, 12 to 13 months

Decorate the refrigerator – Fridge magnets will amuse your baby. Removing and replacing them will enable him to practice grasping objects with his thumb and forefinger and develop

hand-eye coordination. Make sure that the magnets are solidly attached and too big for your baby to swallow (see "Toys and safety," page 366).

The falling tower – Show your baby how to make a tower by stacking up 3 or 4 blocks. Put down the first block, ask him to place the second one, and so on. Then, suggest that he knock over the tower and start again.

Climbing the stairs – When your baby starts to walk, you can teach him a new game that he will like a great deal: going down the stairs backwards.

Nursery rhymes and chatting – To stimulate your baby's acquisition of language, chat with him often. For example, you can entertain him by making a game of identifying the parts of the body. To broaden your repertory, check your municipal library, which may lend children's audiotapes and videocassettes. Children love recited or sung nursery rhymes.

14 to 17 months

Your baby is walking unaided, a source of joy for him and his parents. He is so excited that he is less interested in eating and sleeping. He walks with his legs apart to keep his balance. Now is the time to buy him flexible shoes for walking outside the home (see "Your baby's first shoes," page 56).

This is the beginning of your baby's independence, a very important period for his social development and one that is very demanding for his parents. He is like a tornado! He climbs stairs on all fours and crawls down backwards, rummages in cupboards, climbs on chairs and gets into everything. He learns to unscrew the tops of containers, turn door handles and the pages of a book. If he helps you dress him, he can quickly take off his shoes and throw them. He discovers the principle of gravity, which encourages him to drop objects from his highchair. Throwing things is part of his learning program.

Your baby follows you around and imitates you in your everyday activities, for example, washing yourself, housework, brushing your teeth and meal preparation. Give him a clean rag, a spoon and a bowl. Name his gestures. Ask him to listen and imitate the sounds of cars, airplanes, the vacuum cleaner and animals. He likes to pretend to talk on the telephone. Play music for him.

He will dance to the rhythm. Play tag and hide-and-seek with him. He will be delighted. He loves to play in the sand and splash about in water. Be careful! He puts everything in his mouth, even stones.

He begins to understand simple everyday instructions, for example, "Get your teddy bear." without your gestures. Give him time to speak and encourage him to express himself since he will learn through practice. Complete what he says using short sentences. For example, if he says "fass" you can add "Yes, the top is spinning fast!" Instead of anticipating his desires, let him express his needs.

Activities, 14 to 17 months

Jigsaw puzzles and toolbox – Your child's dexterity is improving and he likes toys that can be assembled and dismantled, and stacking toys. This is the time to give him jigsaw puzzles with big pieces, a plastic toolbox and big building blocks.

Pull toys – He likes to pull, push and move a vehicle. Offer him long-handled toys, wagons, cars, balls and boxes filled with varied objects.

Attach a short string to an empty shoebox and suggest that he take his teddy bear for a sleigh ride.

Bubbles – Blow bubbles in your baby's bath. He will try to catch them. He will be very excited. Be careful, though, he must remain seated. The same game played outdoors on the lawn will be just as exciting.

Drawings – Give him paper and non-toxic crayons. Show him how to scribble. He will immediately understand the link between the gesture and the outcome. Applaud the artist and display his masterpiece on the refrigerator.

18 to 24 months

Your child becomes more and more self-confident and independent. Do you have the impression that he is growing away from you? He is simply discovering the world around him.

Around the age of 18 months, he better understands instructions and simple questions, such as "Where is your coat?" without your gestures. He points to a picture or part of the body when you ask him to. He will soon be able to combine 2 words, for example, "Dada gone." His vocabulary comprises between 50 and 100 words. Around the age of 2 years, it will include nearly 200 words.

You will soon be conversing with your child and discussing with him an event or object. Do not worry if he still cannot pronounce all sounds and syllables. His curiosity is aroused and he asks lots of questions. Listen to him and answer him as simply as possible. This is the ideal opportunity to teach him language.

He chatters, sometimes constantly, and continues to imitate you by feeding his teddy bear, bathing it, making it walk and putting it to sleep. He plays at being daddy. Each day, his dexterity grows. Soon he will be able to line up or stack cubes or even succeed in threading large wooden beads or winding string on a spool.

At the age of 2, he wants to eat, drink and get undressed on his own. He loves to learn. Sometimes he will make a mess, but do not get upset, it is not important. Let him experiment, but keep an eye on him. His successes will give him confidence in his potential.

At the table, he does not like being helped. He holds his spoon properly, although he is still clumsy in bringing it to his mouth. He enjoys splashing soup all over with his spoon. He can easily remove his socks and hat. You can encourage him to dress himself by giving him clothing that is easy to put on.

At this age, your child has a tremendous need to move about. He runs, stops, starts again, stops briefly, feet apart and stomach forward, squats as though he wants to urinate, gets up, sets off again and falls. He bumps himself all over. He can kick a ball. He dances, turning around several times, when he likes the music. He loves to play outdoors. Your child needs room to walk, jump and run as he pleases. When he stops to catch his breath, teach him how to sit cross-legged, a good position for the legs.

Your baby plays with you or an older child, but not with someone his own age. He does not lend his toys but you will gradually encourage him to share them, which is easier when he is 3 or 4 years old.

Activities, 18 to 24 months

A bedtime story every day – As often as possible, take the time to tell your child stories. Point to the words you are reading and he will learn to recognize them. Show him the pictures, ask him to turn the pages and let him handle the book. Your child will discover that you read from left to right and from the top to the bottom of the page and will notice that a story has a beginning and an end. He will express his emotions. Take advantage of this opportunity to share with him precious moments of pleasure and caring. Choose books that are attractive to him. You can borrow books from the library or suggest that family members give him books as gifts.

Other word games – The written word is present everywhere. When you take your baby for a stroll, satisfy his curiosity by reading everything that attracts his attention, such as the names of stores, advertisements, road signs, and so on. He will learn to recognize logos, a first step in deciphering words.

Disguises – Your baby loves to dress up. He borrows grownups' hats and shoes. Set aside clothing for these activities that he can dirty as he pleases.

Bring on the music! – Your baby discovers music. Listen to recordings and sing his favourite songs with him. The songs he prefers are often those accompanied by simple gestures. Since he handles toys more skilfully, you can give him musical instruments such as a drum, xylophone or cymbals.

Improvisation – This is the age for building blocks. Your baby loves finger painting, plasticine and mud pies. Comment on his work as doing so will encourage him to verbalize. Remember to display his work, of which he will be very proud.

Fresh air – Your child needs to move about. He needs room to run and jump. Play with him in the yard or a park as often as you can.

Toilet training

The age at which children are toilet trained varies greatly, although toilet training usually begins around the age of 2 years. Most children can control their stools and urine during the day between the ages of 2 and 4 years. Girls tend to become toilet trained more quickly than boys.

Toilet training takes, on average, between 3 and 6 months. However, we recommend that you do not set a deadline. As long as your child is not ready, it is pointless to force him.

It may be several months or years before the child can control his urine at night.

The conditions necessary for toilet training appear between the ages of 18 months and 3 years. Here are some signs that your child may be ready for this new learning:

- Your child can walk to his pot.

- He is beginning to undress himself unaided (he can take down his pants).

- His diaper stays dry for several hours.

- He understands simple directions such as "Take this to daddy."

- He can express his needs with expressions such as "want milk," which means he may be able to say "go wee-wee."

- He shows that he is proud to be able to do things by himself.

Here is how you can facilitate your child's toilet training:

- Prepare your baby gradually by making him familiar with the names and motions related to elimination: poo, pee, potty and toilet.

- Encourage him to imitate you. Just as he will learn to talk by copying you, he will want to imitate you to go to the toilet. Put his pot near the toilet and encourage him to do as you do. When he is ready, he will feel the desire to copy mommy and daddy.

- Use the pot instead of the toilet during the first stages because your child will feel safer and steadier.

- Make sure that your child is seated comfortably on the pot with his feet on the floor. If he is seated higher, put a small bench under his feet to enable him to relax.

- At first, ask your child to sit fully dressed on the pot, then after his wet diaper has been removed.

- Later, have your child sit on the pot at set times during the day, for example, when he wakes up, after meals or snacks and before naps and bedtime in order to establish a routine.

- Congratulate your child each time he shows an interest in sitting on his pot.

- Once your child has used the pot regularly for several days, change to training or cotton underpants.

- Do not be discouraged by accidental soiling of the underpants as it is inevitable and is part of the training.

- Encourage your child's efforts and avoid punishing him.

Sooner or later, your child will want to use the pot. Do not rush him. Toilet training is easier in the absence of stress.

Avoid active toilet training during a stressful time such as a move from one home to another, a change of sitter or day care, or the arrival or a new sibling.

An important reminder

It is important to respect your child's pace to ensure that this important stage of development is a positive one. Never attempt to toilet train your child before he is physically and emotionally ready for it. Trust him.

Introduction to reading and writing

Now that your child has handled his first books, he begins to awaken to the written word. Long before he starts school, you can help him to discover reading by means of simple situations in everyday life. A child who has frequent contact with the written word will be a better reader and have a better chance of succeeding in school.

Your child observes you and tries to imitate you. When you read and write, do so often in his presence.

- When your baby starts to talk, reproduce his first words in big letters and display them on the refrigerator. Occasionally point to one of these words.

- When he starts to name the people around him, you can write each person's name next to a photo of the person. For example, if he says "dada," write the word in big letters under a picture of his father.

- When he gives you a drawing, write his name at the bottom of it.

Little by little, your child will make the connection between the spoken and written word. He will discover the usefulness of writing and will develop a positive impression of it.

To find out more about the introduction to reading and writing, obtain a copy of the series entitled *Hand in Hand: Emergent Literacy from A to Z* available on the ministère de l'Éducation Web site (see "Resources for parents," "Suggested reading," page 450).

The Family

Fatherhood

Fathers are not born, they are made.

Preparing to play this exciting role from the time of conception means having an opportunity to embark upon a remarkable adventure. This is a secret that a growing number of happy fathers wish to share with their peers. More and more Quebec fathers are expressing the happiness and pride that fatherhood brings them.

They readily agree that not enough is said about paternity. In a society where, not so long ago, fathers were often relegated to the simple role of providers, other models for fatherhood have yet to be invented.

Take your place. You are a unique and important presence in your child's life. By committing yourself early to your newborn, you will find it easier to establish a solid bond with your baby (see "The importance of bonding," page 70). However, you must first decide the role that you want to play in her life.

Perhaps you will have to assert your wish to play such a role, since some mothers are less inclined than others to share responsibility for the newborn.

A new role

For 9 months you have been preparing for your baby's arrival. You have been able to monitor the pregnancy by observing the ultrasound scan, by attending prenatal classes with your partner, and by feeling the baby move in the womb.
You and your partner have anticipated with excitement your child's birth.

Today, your lives have changed dramatically. Your schedule and home have been turned upside down, your partner is tired, and your life as a couple seems to have vanished. In a word, there are no more reference points. **Do not panic. Most parents go through this phase.**

Like so many other fathers before, you will adapt to this new, seemingly disruptive life.

Name your emotions – The birth of a child can arouse a wide range of emotions. The first step is to acknowledge them. Some men want to flee: they throw themselves into their work, sports or new projects. The desire to escape sometimes masks the fear of making a commitment. It may be hard to recognize and understand your emotions, but it is essential that you do, and that you express and communicate them in a healthy way. Doing so will enable you to begin the process of adapting to your role as a father.

Take part in caring for your baby – There is no easy formula for becoming a perfect parent. You will learn to have faith in yourself by participating in your baby's everyday care. You will discover your ways of doing things, which may differ from those of your partner.

What is important is that you both agree on shared values and the anticipated results.

Maintain your intimacy as a couple – Initially, parents sometimes have the impression that they are constantly on the go and that they can no longer share even a meal together. A couple's identity is put through the mill. Do not worry: when each of you has established a routine, things will be easier. Plan for moments of respite together. Try to understand what is happening to your partner during the post-partum period (see "Motherhood," page 120). When you have adapted to your new roles you will regain your desire for intimacy, although not always at the same time.

Accept help from the family circle – Support from your family and friends can be valuable during this period of adaptation. Accept their offers of help; however, do not let them overwhelm you. Delegate household tasks and meal preparation. Make sure that you maintain the routine you need to become familiar with your new responsibilities. It is also important to protect both the couple's and the family's intimacy.

Advice from dads

Based on several years of successful fatherhood, fathers offer this advice.

- Adopt clear procedures for doing things as a couple.

- Pinpoint each partner's skills.

- Indicate how you would like to participate in caring for your baby.

- Above all, remember to give yourself a chance to:

  - learn;
  - grow as a father;
  - be different as parents, that is, as a father and a mother.

Despite everything, difficult moments will arise. The baby's arrival is not always what you expect.

You will worry. That's part of parenting. So are imperfections. Enjoy your own growth too, for parenting is learned day by day. Over time you will become the parent you want to be.

Here are some tips from fathers: "I talk to another father who is going through a similar experience," says one dad. "I rely on my inner strengths and beliefs," adds another.

Your partner's trust and support will help you to discover your new identity and assume your responsibilities as a father. You can also share your experience with other couples in a similar situation. If you do not know any, contact the nearest CLSC.

When your everyday and working lives are back to normal, remember, above all, to reserve pleasant moments:

- for you;
- for you and your partner;
- with your child.

Feeding your baby together, as a couple

During the first 6 months, breast-feeding is by far the best for your baby. You can play a key role both for your partner and your child. A mother who is breast-feeding needs encouragement, especially if she is going through a difficult period.

You can contribute to successful breast-feeding by taking charge of household tasks such as grocery shopping, cooking and laundry. You can take advantage of this period to get to know your baby by changing her diaper, holding her, rocking her, singing to her, bathing her, or simply carrying her to her mother for nursing.

You can then hold her on your chest to put her to sleep. All children, regardless of sex, need reassuring, comforting physical contact with their father.

Importance of the father-child relationship

While the father-child relationship is different from the mother-child relationship, it is very important for both girls and boys. A father often establishes special bonds with a newborn by playing with her. Such bonds will become more important over time. A father provides a model that is different from that of the mother. He likes to play actively with his child, is usually stricter, and is often more inclined to encourage the child to explore her environment and search for independence.

The quality of the father-child relationship unquestionably affects interaction between the child and her peers and adults.

However, both parents must agree on family rules and their application. A harmonious approach to discipline will be valuable in the future. It is easier to be a parent when the parents can rely on each other. It is more enriching for the entire family.

Fathers everywhere

Community agencies, medical clinics, CLSCs, childcare centres and other family-oriented facilities more broadly recognize the role played by fathers and offer them support.

As a father, you can also request that they call upon you to make an appointment or participate in an activity. This practice is still not widespread, but by requesting it you will help to broaden the presence of fathers in the lives of their children.

If you are interested, you can join a fathers' group. Such groups have been established in several regions of Quebec. Contact the nearest CLSC or family centre (see "Associations, agencies and support groups," page 443).

Let your children teach you your role. They do not expect you to be perfect but to be present.

What they are saying is, **"A father is important everywhere, always and all of the time."**

We encourage fathers to read the chapter entitled "Motherhood" in order to explore the differences and particularities of motherhood. Do not hesitate to ask questions and to listen attentively to your partner so that you can discover together these new facets of your adult lives.

Motherhood

The birth of a child sparks a broad range of emotions. Your body and your life are disrupted. You ask yourself a lot of questions. You may occasionally feel discouraged, alone in the world or suffer from baby blues. All of this is part of the process of adapting to your baby and learning what motherhood is all about.

After the birth of your baby, as was true during pregnancy and birth, you may need the advice or assistance of a professional. The following sections provide answers to the questions that mothers ask most frequently. To further explore the joys of family life, we encourage you to read the sections on child development and other chapters in the section devoted to the family. A new chapter entitled "Fatherhood" has been written specially for your partner.

Depression and baby blues

Have you experienced sudden changes of mood and crying fits since your baby was born? Do you feel overwhelmed and exhausted and ask yourself whether having a baby was such a good idea? This is normal. You are tired and almost all new mothers experience the blues for brief periods of time. The post-partum blues last several hours, several days or up to 2 weeks. During this adjustment to your new life as a mother, try following these tips.

- Get out in the sun.

- Discuss your feelings with your partner or another loved one.

- Contact other parents.

- Dress up and take care of yourself.

- Allow yourself short breaks and get out of the house with your baby.

- Try to temporarily obtain additional assistance from your loved ones.

- Encourage contact between your skin and your baby's skin and savour happy moments.

This will usually suffice to overcome the blues. However, if you have felt depressed every day for several weeks, are suffering from insomnia and loss of appetite and are losing interest in your baby and other people, you are perhaps suffering from post-partum depression. Consult a doctor or psychologist promptly; either can help bring a smile back to your face and enable you to fully enjoy motherhood.

The importance of rest

To recover physically and emotionally from childbirth, new mothers need plenty of rest. You are tired and this is normal. It will take several weeks to regain your normal energy level. Be patient, take care of yourself and do not hesitate to ask for help when you need it.

Use the first few days following your baby's birth to rest. Adjust your rest periods to your baby's feeding schedule. Stay in bed and, if possible, only get up to wash yourself, eat and take care of the baby. Your partner can help you change the baby's diaper and carry him to you to nurse. If he is absent, ask a family member or friend to help you during the first days so that you can rest. **You should not plan other activities during the first week after your baby's birth.**

You will need help up to the third week to take care of housework, cooking and other children.

Your baby will often wake you up during the night. This is a good reason to rest when he sleeps during the day. Depending on your needs, you can take 2 naps every day during the first week, then once a day until at least the sixth week or as long as your baby wakes up at night.

Physical recovery

Blood loss

For 1 or 2 days after giving birth, blood loss (lochia) will be more abundant than during menstruation. The bleeding will then diminish and change texture. It may be mixed with mucus, a whitish substance. The colour will change gradually from pinkish to increasingly pale brown.

You may occasionally discharge a blood clot, above all in the morning after urinating or breast-feeding. An unusual effort and a Caesarean section can also cause redder, more abundant lochia. The resumption of bleeding, approximately 10 days after childbirth, stems from the healing of the placenta site.

Lochia usually lasts for 3 to 6 weeks. Do not use tampons during this period. Instead, buy sanitary napkins without plastic linings since the linings can be irritating.

An important reminder

Consult your doctor or midwife if:

* you soak 2 sanitary napkins in less than an hour;
* you discharge several blood clots bigger than an egg;
* the discharges are foul-smelling;
* your temperature exceeds 38.5°C (101.3°F).

Contractions

You will perhaps feel uterine after-pains, especially when you nurse your baby. If you need to relieve the pain, consult your doctor or midwife.

Healing of the perineum

Your perineum will be sensitive for some time, especially if stitches were necessary after the birth. You may experience a burning sensation when urinating. Do not hesitate to splash warm water on the vulva as you urinate. Relax when you have a bowel movement. Do not be afraid, your stitches will not break. To soothe the tingling sensation, you can take a 10- to 15-minute bath once or twice a day. Let the stitches dry before getting dressed.

Hygiene

You can safely take baths the first week after giving birth. Hygiene is very important. To avoid health problems, follow these recommendations:

- take a shower or bath every day in a clean bathtub without bath oil or bubble bath;

- change your sanitary napkin at least every 4 hours;

- always wipe yourself from front to back;

- wash your hands after using the toilet.

However, do not give yourself a vaginal douche. Moreover, avoid swimming as long as lochia or heavy discharges persist.

Exercise

To restore tone to your body after pregnancy and childbirth, you can exercise the perineum. Several times a day, contract the muscles of the pelvic floor, as though you were holding in urine, and then release them. Do a series of exercises the day after giving birth. Gradually work up to 100 contractions per day toward the end of the first week.

Wait for several weeks before undertaking an exercise program to restore your figure. Avoid overly long walks. If you leave the house, remember that you will tire more readily, perhaps even suddenly. Pace yourself.

Healthy weight

Most women regain their normal weight almost effortlessly. Within several months at the most, your body will exhaust the reserves accumulated during pregnancy. Maintain a healthy diet. Two months after giving birth, you can gradually resume physical activity. Be patient. The weight you have gained in 9 months cannot be eliminated in a few days.

Resist the temptation to lose weight quickly, above all if you are breast-feeding. It is reasonable to lose between 1 and 2 kg (2 to 4 lb.) per month. **Do not follow a drastic weight-reduction program if you are breast-feeding.** A calorie-reduced diet can curtail your milk production and lower your energy level.

Sexual desire

Some women say that their sexual desire diminishes after the birth of a baby. Fatigue, adaptation to your parental role, the time you devote to caring for your child, physical or emotional complications and hormonal changes all explain reduced sexual desire. Once you have adapted to the situation, you should once again enjoy intimacy and sexual relations with your partner.

Most couples resume sexual relations several weeks after childbirth. You can wait even longer if your vagina or perineum continues to be sensitive, if you are still bleeding, or if you are very tired. Follow your own pace. Motherhood affords you an opportunity to discover a different kind of intimacy, filled with caresses, kisses and affectionate gestures. Do not wait to have a lot of free time to allow yourself intimate moments together. You will quickly learn to take advantage of the precious moments that your baby allows while he is sleeping.

During breast-feeding, your body releases hormones that can prevent your vagina from properly lubricating itself. If need be, use a water-based lubricant to facilitate caressing of the genital organs and penetration.

Contraception

Giving birth to a child demands a great deal of energy. If possible, avoid getting pregnant again too soon. Do not hesitate to consult your doctor or midwife for family planning assistance. If you are not breast-feeding, consider seeking advice promptly since ovulation usually resumes between the third and sixth week after childbirth.

Do not rely solely on breast-feeding to avoid getting pregnant. Breast-feeding is not a reliable birth control method. However, since breast-feeding delays ovulation, it can prevent pregnancy 98% of the time when all of the following conditions are met:

- the mother has not menstruated or lost blood after the 56th day (8 weeks) following childbirth;

- she is exclusively breast-feeding day and night an infant under 6 months of age (the child is not consuming any other milk or food and is not using a pacifier);

- the baby does not sleep more than 6 consecutive hours at night.

If any of these conditions is not or is no longer met, do not take chances. Use an effective contraceptive method.

Birth control methods during breast-feeding

Here are 3 preferred birth control methods:

- immediately after giving birth, use a condom with additional lubricant and spermicidal foam, although the foam can be irritating;

- 4 to 6 weeks after childbirth, your doctor can insert an intrauterine device (IUD);

- 6 to 8 weeks after giving birth, when the uterus and vagina have regained their shape, you can use a diaphragm. However, ask your gynaecologist to check that it is properly adjusted to ensure its effectiveness.

Do not use the conventional contraceptive pill that combines estrogen and progesterone before you have weaned your baby, since it reduces milk production. However, the birth-control pill Micronor (Norethindrone) is a better choice. Your doctor might also suggest progesterone implants and injections.

If you prefer natural contraception methods such as the Billings and sympto-thermic methods, first consult Serena (see "Useful addresses," page 444), your CLSC, doctor or midwife. These methods demand attention but are effective and can be very satisfactory.

Breast-feeding or not

You can speak to your doctor about an innovative intrauterin system that offers up to 5 years of reliable contraceptio

– May reduce volume and duration of your menstrual period

– Can be fitted 6 weeks after delivery and is reversible at any time

– IUDs are among the 1st choice in contraception following childbirth*

* See the contraception section in this book for more opti

Contraceptive methods for mothers who are not breast-feeding

All of the methods mentioned earlier are suitable. Since you are not breast-feeding, you can also take the birth control pill. However, if possible, wait until menstruation resumes. This means that your menstrual cycle is re-establishing itself normally. You can also opt for natural contraceptive methods such as the Billings and sympto-thermic methods, which make it easier to recognize when fertility resumes.

In an emergency

If you have engaged in poorly protected or unprotected sex, you can resort to the emergency contraceptive methods indicated below.

- The intrauterine device: if it is not counterindicated, the IUD can be inserted by your gynaecologist up to 7 days after sexual intercourse.

- The morning-after contraceptive pill: it is used up to 5 days after sexual intercourse. The sooner it is taken after intercourse, the more effective it is. Your pharmacist can prescribe the pill and has been trained to do so since January 2002.

An important reminder

The morning-after contraceptive pill does not affect breast-feeding and it is, therefore, advantageous to use it during breast-feeding. However, if the morning-after contraceptive pill also contains estrogen, it can briefly reduce milk production. Consult a self-help group, a breast-feeding consultant or a CLSC nurse to help you restore milk production.

Breast-feeding and diet

Your diet does not have to be perfect in order to produce quality milk. However, you must eat properly to re-establish your nutritional reserves after pregnancy and childbirth and to avoid exhaustion.

In addition to 3 meals a day, a breast-feeding mother must have several snacks, depending on her appetite. Eat healthy food. Fruits, vegetables, muffins, bread, nuts, cheese and yogurt are good choices.

Maintain adequate portion sizes, as you did during pregnancy. Follow *Canada's Food Guide to Healthy Eating* to ensure that you obtain all of the necessary nutrients. Remember the 4 food groups: grain products, vegetables and fruit, meat and alternatives, and milk products.

Generally speaking, a mother who eats properly does not need to take vitamin or mineral supplements, even while breast-feeding.

Milk products

Milk products provide protein and calcium, two nutrients that are very important for breast-feeding. Breast-feeding mothers should consume 3 or 4 portions a day. If you do not like milk, replace it with cheese or yogurt. Soy-based drinks do not have the same nutritional value as dairy products, but enriched soy products provide the same amount of calcium and vitamin D as milk.

Fish

Some fish species absorb pollutants, which enter breast milk and can harm the baby. The following species should not be consumed more than once a month: swordfish, shark, and fresh or frozen tuna (the restriction does not apply to canned tuna). Avoid bass, northern pike, walleyed pike, muskellunge, lake trout, lobster tomalley (liver), caviar, and fish liver.

Water

Quench your thirst. Drink water, milk, fruit or vegetable juice, herbal tea and broth. If your urine is dark or cloudy, it means that you are not drinking enough. However, drinking large amounts will not increase the amount of milk you produce.

Coffee and herbal teas

Caffeine enters breast milk. Excessive amounts of coffee, tea and cola-type soft drinks can make some babies nervous and irritable. Drink only moderate amounts of the beverages: up to 2 cups a day. Decaffeinated products do not pose a problem.

You can replace coffee with cereal-based beverages or herbal teas. Chicory, linden, mint, wild rose and fruit herbal teas are good choices. Allow them to steep for not more than 3 to 5 minutes.

An important reminder

- Breast-feeding does not mean depriving yourself. Some foods alter the taste of milk, but infants adapt to it. However, a baby may react badly to certain foods. If you think this is the case, stop eating the foods for several days, then reintroduce them while monitoring your child's reactions (see "Colic and milk intolerance," page 294).

- To our knowledge, no food increases the production of mother's milk. However, if you feel tired, a milk-based drink can provide you with calories and nutrients that will boost your energy.

- If allergies are frequent in your family, reduce the risk of your baby's developing them by avoiding the most allergenic foods (see "Preventing allergies," page 301). If your baby is diagnosed with an allergy, you must change your diet. Ask a dietitian/nutritionist to rebalance it.

- If you are a vegan, that is, you do not eat any animal products (meat, fish, eggs and dairy products) and you are breast-feeding, you must take a vitamin B_{12} supplement. Consume foods that are rich in protein, iron, calcium and vitamin D. It is advisable to consult a dietitian/nutritionist, who will recommend supplements, if need be.

Constipation

It is normal not to have a bowel movement for 2 or 3 days after a vaginal birth and 3 to 5 days after a Caesarean section. However, beyond that time, you may be constipated. This often occurs after childbirth because of the pain stemming from the episiotomy, hormones, the medication administered, a lack of activity and dehydration. If you are constipated:

- eat fibre-rich foods such as bran cereal, whole-grain bread, vegetables, fruits, legumes and nuts;

- drink plenty of fluids;

- go to the toilet as soon as you feel the need to;

- drink prune juice or eat prunes.

If these measures are not enough, use a laxative. Choose a fibre-based product such as Metamucil. As a last resort, take mineral oil (available from a pharmacy) before bedtime, but only for short periods. Other laxatives can upset the mother or baby.

Family Life

Giving birth to a child is a joy and a source of wonder, but also of worry and doubt. Life changes completely. It takes a certain amount of time to adapt to it. Stay calm and have confidence in yourself.

Your baby will help you. Observe her closely. In no time, you will learn about her temperament, tastes, the way she likes to be cared for and caressed. Through her gestures, she will show you that she is happy or unhappy. Every time you dry her tears, you will feel more assured and more at ease in your role as a parent. The mutual trust that is established between you and your baby will strengthen your attachment to each other.

No need to be perfect

Accept that you cannot be perfect. To be a parent is to accept making mistakes and knowing how to correct them. Congratulate yourself when things go well. You will perhaps occasionally have the impression that you forget yourself completely when taking care of your child. At other times, your baby will give you enormous pleasure that will boost your energy and make you proud of yourself and of her.

Until the age of 2 years, babies grow at a prodigious pace. Every day, they learn something new. So do you! Parenthood is demanding and exciting. You will discover unsuspected talents and qualities in yourself. Of course, you will sometimes be tired.

Babies display almost inexhaustible physical energy, which is not true of adults. Do not be discouraged. Little by little, with sleep, free time and exercise, you will once again be in top form.

Invest in your relationship as a couple

Do not overlook your relationship as a couple, for your sake and that of your child. As soon as you feel the need, organize an outing or a day off. Continue to share entertaining activities or engage in joint projects. Enjoy yourselves!

Communication is a good way to sustain your relationship as a couple. The period following pregnancy implies changes and requires adaptation by both parents. For this reason, it is important to discuss the emotions, uncertainty and great joy that you feel during this period in order to maintain close ties.

New family situations

If your family is a blended family, you have already experienced certain stages of adaptation. Your new baby is part of a family that probably already has one or more children and its own characteristics. Each family situation warrants paying the necessary attention to ensure that each family member feels welcome, at ease and happy.

The arrival of a baby will afford you an opportunity to discuss once again each family member's place. There is no pat formula. It is up to you to discover what suits each member of your family. Blended families are becoming increasingly numerous. Do not hesitate to discuss your situation with your friends and colleagues. Family life is very enriching but it is also sometimes demanding. If you need support, contact your CLSC or a community agency. You can also consult books on this topic.

Reaction of older children

The arrival of a baby can be an unsettling event for a child. It is important to prepare the older child before the baby is born. Even when older children are properly prepared, their behaviour may change for several weeks. They need time to get used to their new role and make sure that you still love them.

The older child may start to wet the bed again, suck his thumb, stutter, or ask to nurse. Do not reprimand the child. Continue to show tenderness toward him: he will quickly become attached to the infant. He will feel valued helping you in a grown-up way if you involve him in all sorts of small tasks. You can explain to him what you are doing when caring for the baby and remind him that you cared for him the same way when he was an infant. If he still enjoys it, rock him, sing to him and tell him that you love him just as much as you did before the new baby arrived.

Doing so will make him feel proud. Make sure that family members and friends take as much interest in the older child as in the baby. A small gesture of attention will make him happy.

Twins

If you give birth to twins, during the first months, your life will revolve around feeding, diapers, baths and sleep. You will carry out the same routine as all parents, only doubly so.

While your twins resemble each other, they are 2 separate people. Dress them differently so that family and friends are less likely to confuse them. Give them dissimilar first names. In this way, each child will know that she is unique. Even though they are identical, the babies will probably have different schedules. To help you, make a note of each twin's schedule. This will also be very useful to family members and friends who give you a hand.

When friends ask you to suggest gifts, you could request diapers, cooked meals or a few hours of respite. You will undoubtedly need help in caring for the babies and in performing household tasks. Seek help from your family, friends and your CLSC. Put a list on the refrigerator of things to do, to guide your helpful Samaritans.

You can breast-feed your twins. Your body will readily produce milk to satisfy them. Breast-feeding is just as desirable for twins as for a single child and allows you to establish close contact with each one.

Even if you are the parents of twins or triplets and are thus very busy, be sure that you set aside time for yourselves. You are not just parents. Get out of the house to break the routine and chat with other people. Moreover, your twins will arouse widespread admiration that will make you very proud and reward all your efforts.

Photo: Linda Vaillant

To obtain additional information, contact the Montreals Parents' of Twins Association (see "Useful addresses," page 444).

Sharing tasks

During the first months of your baby's life, you will often have the impression that you are short of time. Work as a team. Share responsibilities in light of your tastes and schedules and your pleasures, too. If either of you feels overwhelmed and has to request help from his or her mate each day, your relationship as a couple will suffer. Clearly defined, fair sharing of tasks will help maintain harmony.

All parents need respite. Both parents should spend time alone with the baby and have time to themselves. Try to get out of the house once in awhile. Disconnect the telephone, if need be. Do not hesitate to request assistance from community agencies, the CLSC or organizations that offer services to new parents.

Baby's first outings

Your baby needs air, light and outings. In the winter, a healthy baby can be taken outdoors every day, provided that the temperature is not below -12°C (10°F) and that it is not too windy. Such outings provide pleasure, distraction and fresh air.

The first outing must be short, no longer than 20 to 30 minutes. Protect her from the wind by putting up the top of the baby carriage.

In the summer, babies find heat unbearable and must not be exposed to the sun (see "In the sun," page 370). When it is very hot, that is, 25°C (77°F) or more, dress your baby lightly in a top and a diaper. You can leave the window open in her room when she is sleeping. When the temperature is around 21°C (72°F), she can sleep outside in a baby carriage with mosquito netting, sheltered from the wind and sun. The baby carriage must be big enough to allow the baby to lie stretched out. Always strap the baby into the carriage and keep an eye on her.

Family activities

Your energy will return after the period of adaptation. Some parents feel a need to organize family outings. Do not deprive yourselves of such outings. Life must not cease with the birth of a baby. Regardless of whether you have 1, 2 or 3 children, outings are good for everyone. They strengthen family ties. They make adults feel fulfilled and contented. They break the isolation of parents who remain in the home. Try to organize brief outings as soon as you have the urge.

Most children like to be outdoors. Go for walks with them in the stroller in the summer and a sleigh in the winter. Summertime picnics in the park are pleasant. If the weather is bad, enjoy brief visits with family and friends.

What kind of outings can be organized with a small child? The choice is up to you. Municipalities often organize pleasant, inexpensive activities, for example, public swimming pools, storytelling at the public library and children's shows. Contact the recreation department to find out more.

Ask your friends with young children what their favourite family activities are. Enjoy yourselves!

Get a babysitter

Mom, do you want to get out by yourself, go for a walk or visit friends? Your partner is the best person to take care of your baby. This will afford him an opportunity to be alone with the child and display his skills as a father. It is a special time. If you both wish to go out, you will have to entrust your baby to someone else. Choose someone who is recommended by other parents.

Choosing a day-care service

Educational day-care services play an important role. They contribute to your child's development. They have become essential for many parents who must reconcile family and work obligations.

Before you choose a day-care service, pinpoint your needs and expectations. Think about your educational values, your child's needs and the services available. Find out if the day-care service offers interesting activities and allows children to play outdoors. If possible, register your infant with a service where there are other children the same age so that she does not lack stimulation.

Choose a day-care service carefully. Your child's well-being depends on it. Start your research early. You must often wait several months to obtain a place in a day-care centre.

Do not be surprised if your baby is sick more frequently. Her immune system has not fully developed and contact with other children increases the risk of infection. However, colds and diarrhoea will most likely enable your baby to produce antibodies that will protect her later on.

Day-care services

- **Child-care centres** – They provide educational child care in a facility that must include safe play areas inside and outside and comply with the educational program of the ministère de l'Emploi, de la Solidarité sociale et de la Famille. Children are divided into groups by age and supervised by a team of educators. Such services cost $7 a day.

- **Educational home child care governed by a child-care centre** – An independent worker who supervises between 6 and 9 children in her home cares for your child. The home must include safe play areas inside and outside and comply with the educational program of the ministère de l'Emploi, de la Solidarité sociale et de la Famille. Home child care costs $7 a day.

- **Day-care centres** – In Quebec, a day-care centre is a private, for-profit service. Some day-care centres offer places at $7 a day or more. They must comply with the educational program of the ministère de l'Emploi, de la Solidarité sociale et de la Famille.

- **Private babysitters** – After interviewing several candidates, you choose the person who will care for your child in your home. Rates vary. Some people without special training offer to care for children in their own homes. Be cautious since their skills vary.

It is preferable to choose a service in your neighbourhood, near your place of work or on the way to work. In this way, you will save time and spend valuable moments with your child.

A visit is essential

Before you entrust your baby to a day-care service, meet with your child's future educator. Ask about the age of the children cared for, the educational program and the quality of meals. Take advantage of this opportunity to visit the service and observe whether it is safe and the staff act with the children in a manner that suits you.

Remember to ask which services the facility can offer and at what cost.

Make sure that the facility complies with the basic rules of hygiene. It must be clean and airy. The washing of hands and toys must be an integral part of the service's routine. To facilitate your child's integration, a visit with your child will enable you to observe the educator's approach and your child's reactions to her. Following this visit, have your child participate in certain routines at the centre. For example, snack- and meal-time and nap-time are ideal moments to enable your child to adapt to a new person. Avoid overly long periods of day care on the first days to enable your child to adapt gradually.

An important reminder

- Do not allow a teenager under the age of 14 to babysit a newborn. Do not leave a newborn alone with another child.

- When you need an occasional babysitter, choose someone with experience who has taken a babysitting course (see "Web sites," page 447). Have the babysitter visit your home before entrusting your child to the person and observe how your child reacts to the babysitter.

- Before you choose a babysitter or day-care service, ask for information and references.

Overcoming isolation

The discomfort experienced at the end of a pregnancy can cause couples to withdraw from social life. It feels so good to be in your own home, quiet and comfortably propped up by a mountain of pillows. When your baby arrives, her routine will further isolate you. Getting out of the house seems so complicated that you prefer to stay at home. Get a move on! Spending the entire day alone with the baby can be depressing. Motherhood and fatherhood are much easier when you have friends.

You will quickly invent a new way to interact with those around you. Be adventurous. Bundle up your baby and take a stroll in your neighbourhood. Your newborn will attract attention. Make the most of it by chatting with your neighbours. Take part in a self-help group for young families. Invite a friend, a loved one or another couple to share your day-to-day routine. Many people love to pamper a baby. Their generosity will surprise you. Perhaps you will discover the perfect babysitter.

Little by little, your social network will grow and help you assume parenthood smoothly. Your baby needs to have people around her and so do you. Away you go!

Support groups

A number of groups are dedicated to helping young families. Some of the groups focus on parent-child relations in general while others deal with specific needs. Contact the nearest CLSC for more information.

Mothers can rely on breast-feeding support groups. Do not hesitate to contact them.

They can offer valuable advice. They have helped many women overcome problems and successfully breast-feed their babies (see "Breast-feeding resources," page 454).

There are also self-help groups for fathers, which play an important role by fostering discussion and reflection, while creating a new model for fatherhood.

Community organizations

Many community groups offer services to new families. Are you aware of them?

These community organizations, volunteer groups and enterprises in the social economy have developed over the years to support parents in assuming their new occupation. Do not hesitate

to contact them. Their staff has the necessary skills. In many ways, they can help make life that much easier for you and your baby.

Specifically, they offer the following types of support:

- prenatal classes to prepare you for the birth of your baby;
- a qualified attendant to support you during childbirth;
- breast-feeding support;
- household help for everyday tasks or to entertain other children;
- get-togethers for parents to share experiences;
- support in educating your child;
- activities for parents and children;
- workshops and talks, and so on.

You can take advantage of these services when you are pregnant. In this way, you will be fully prepared to welcome your baby. However, it is never too late to obtain information. You will always be parents.

Sharing with members of your community can be enriching for you and for other parents at every stage of your life. Contact your CLSC to find out about organizations in your neighbourhood. It can provide information, assistance, respite, solutions, friends, a babysitter or even encourage you to become a volunteer.

Services offered by CLSCs

As the slogan says, your CLSC is for life. Everyone, from newborns to the elderly, can benefit from CLSC services, which vary from one region to the next. However, all CLSCs focus on young families.

You can visit your CLSC as soon as you become pregnant. It organizes prenatal classes that prepare you to enjoy a healthy pregnancy and birth and enable both parents to assume their parental role. If you are experiencing financial problems, you may be eligible to receive milk, eggs and oranges during your pregnancy under the OLO ("eggs, milk and oranges") program.

Several days after the birth of your baby, you can request that a CLSC nurse visit you at home to ensure that everything is going well for both of you. If you wish, you can participate in breast-feeding clinics. When your infant receives her first vaccination at the age of 2 months, it is the ideal time to ask the nurse about your baby's diet, sleeping habits and development. The nurse is a reliable source of information.

If you are finding it difficult to adapt to motherhood or fatherhood, the CLSC can help you get through this difficult period. You may have access to services such as home visits, respite care, parental support, and parent-children stimulation groups.

The CLSCs collaborate with child care centres in the day-care network to help you, when necessary. They also work in collaboration with community organizations that support young families. If need be, they will direct you to the appropriate community services.

Your CLSC's Info-Santé health information line is an excellent resource and reassurance, especially when you're worried about your child's health. Someone is there 24 hours a day to take your call.

Financial difficulties

The arrival of a child can upset a family in several ways, including financially. Higher expenses and a drop in income stemming from maternal leave can be a source of additional stress.

There are several forms of government economic support to which you are perhaps entitled. The main ones are indicated below. Changes in the programs effective January 2005 are indicated in brackets below: child tax benefits, family allowances (child-support program), Parental Wage Assistance Program (work bonus), and support to enable employment assistance beneficiaries to purchase commercial infant formula. All of the programs are listed in the guide *Become Parent*, available free of charge from Communication Québec.

If your family is having difficulty adjusting financially to the baby's arrival, for example, because of indebtedness or problems paying everyday and other bills, there are 30 or so consumer associations in Quebec that can offer free budgeting consultation services. To find the one nearest you, contact the Union des Consommateurs du Québec at (514) 521-6820 or the Coalition des Associations de Consommateurs du Québec at

(514) 362-8623. You can also consult a directory of the associations at www.consommateur.qc.ca.

The ACEF de l'Est de Montréal, a consumer association, has published a guide on the cost of a new child and key warnings concerning commercial practices aimed at new parents (RESPs, photographs, cotton diapers, and so on). The guide costs $5 and you can order it by calling (514) 257-6622 (add $2 for postage).

Income support

A mother receiving employment assistance (social aid) who decides to breast-feed her baby is eligible for a special breast-feeding allowance of $55 a month until the child reaches the age of 1 year. Mothers who do not breast-feed receive financial assistance to purchase infant formula until the baby is 9 months old, or 1 year old if the child's state of health so requires.

Under this measure, commercial infant formula does not cost any more than cow's milk.

To find out about these measures, call the nearest local employment centre as soon as your baby is born (see the blue section in the telephone directory and look for "Government of Quebec" and the heading "Financial Assistance").

Drug insurance

If your baby suffers from milk intolerance and the doctor prescribes a special formula, this expense may be reimbursed by the Quebec government drug insurance plan or your private plan. Contact the Régie de l'assurance maladie du Québec (RAMQ) or your insurance company.

Assistance

La ligne parents

If you are suddenly worried about your child, consider calling La ligne parents at 1 800 361-5085 or (514) 288-5555. This free counselling service is available throughout Quebec. Do not hesitate to call. Even if the situation does not seem critical, staff will be pleased to provide you with information. In the Montréal area, you can also contact Éducation coup-de-fil at (514) 525-2573.

Info-Parents Guide

A good reference is the Guide Info-Parents, published by Sainte-Justine Hospital. Three volumes are devoted to a list of books, associations and Web sites addressing parental concerns and questions (see "Suggested readings," page 447).

Adaptation problems

Is your child having trouble sleeping or experiencing behavioural problems? Is she excessively nervous or sad? You can talk to a doctor or a trusted professional. Do not feel guilty; after all, you do not hesitate to consult a health professional when your child has an earache. A CLSC social worker can help or direct you to the appropriate assistance. The Ordre des psychologues du Québec can also refer psychologists in your area who work with children. If your budget is limited, some insurance policies and most employee assistance programs partially reimburse such expenses.

Specialized services

Do you think your child needs specialized care? Various professionals can help (see "Who can help your baby?" page 314).

Feeding Your Baby

Cross-cradle position

Breast-feeding

Learning the art of breast-feeding

If breast-feeding seems particularly complicated, it is because the bottle-feeding culture still dominates our modern world and what was once a universal skill has been forgotten. What could be more natural than to breast-feed your newborn?

When young mothers who are breast-feeding today see their granddaughters breast-feed in turn, we will have regained this forgotten skill. Most of the advice given here will no longer be necessary because it will be transmitted from mother to daughter and integrated into the dominant culture. In this way, the breast-feeding culture will be restored. Even now, a majority of Québec mothers breast-feed their infants. You alone can offer your baby this precious food!

Have confidence in yourself. **You are fully capable of breast-feeding your baby**. Breast-feeding is more than a question of technique. It underpins a physical and emotional relationship that develops between your baby and you.

It is normal for you to initially need help. To ensure that breast-feeding begins properly, the first days are very important. Fortunately, practices in hospitals and CLSCs have been modified to offer you better support.

When to consult a professional

While breast-feeding is a natural process, it can occasionally cause problems. You will often find the solution with experience. Self-help groups are especially useful in providing information and general advice (see "Breast-feeding resources," page 454). CLSC nurses, breast-feeding consultants, physicians and midwives can also provide advice.

Consult a trained and experienced breast-feeding specialist if you have any of the following problems:

- difficulty in latching on;

- insufficient weight gain or lack of milk;

- pain and/or injured nipples or breasts.

Breast milk, the ideal food for your baby

Breast milk is the best food for your baby. No other type of milk is equivalent to it. You can decide to breast-feed for several hours, several days, several months or more than a year. The decision is yours to make. Be that as it may, give yourself the opportunity to engage in a unique experience.

Health professionals the world over recommend that infants be breast-fed for at least 1 year. They maintain that babies should be **exclusively breast-fed during the first 6 months** and subsequently as long as the mother and child wish.

Mother's milk is a living, fresh food that is transmitted directly from mother to child. It is the ultimate natural food that is adapted to your baby's needs, comforting for him and rewarding for his mother. It stimulates your baby's development, helps his digestive and immune systems to mature, and protects him from several infections, diseases and allergies.

A food adapted to the child

Breast milk adapts itself to the child's needs.

Colostrum, the milk produced in the first days after birth, is thick and sweet. It is very rich in proteins, vitamins and minerals and perfectly nourishes the baby. It provides numerous antibodies that help the baby combat infections and eliminate from his intestine residues that accumulated before birth.

Subsequently, during lactogenesis, the milk is more fluid, bluish or yellowish white and almost transparent. Its content varies during feeding and in the course of the day. When your baby starts nursing, the milk contains more water, which quenches his thirst. Minutes later, it becomes richer in proteins and fat to satisfy the baby's hunger. Its composition also changes slightly in the subsequent weeks and months to adapt to your baby's needs.

An organic food

Breast milk is highly nourishing. It is easy to digest, very well absorbed and leaves few residues. It is made up of highly digestible, non-allergenic proteins, readily assimilable sugars and iron, and enzymes that facilitate the digestion of fats.

It is produced to satisfy each baby's needs. It provides your infant with the fats he needs and exactly the right amount of vitamins and minerals necessary for his development. Moreover, it is adapted to the maturity of the baby's kidneys.

Mother's milk also contains large amounts of the essential fatty acids linoleic and linolenic acid, which, with the principal sugar, lactose, contribute to the brain's development. Other fatty acids are deposited in the brain during the first months of your baby's life, which fosters, in particular, the development of eyesight.

Babies like breast milk. Its taste varies slightly depending on the mother's diet, which introduces the baby to different flavours.

It is so complete that during the first 6 months, most breast-fed babies do not require any other food. It is subsequently the best choice, complemented gradually by the introduction of solid food (see "Solid food," page 240).

Protection from disease

Mother's milk also provides the baby with various substances that protect him from disease. The longer the mother breast-feeds, the greater the protection, all the more so if the baby is exclusively breast-fed for the first 6 months.

Compared with other babies, breast-fed infants are less subject to gastroenteritis, diarrhoea, respiratory tract illnesses such as laryngitis and bronchitis, colds, otitis and meningitis. When such illnesses do occur, they are less serious and less frequently require hospitalization. Breast-fed babies are also better protected from a number of chronic ailments, such as obesity, Crohn's disease, ulcerative colitis, diabetes and leukemia. Infants who have consumed only mother's milk up to the age of 6 months suffer less often from anaemia and are more resistant to allergies.

Mothers who breast-feed are also subject to fewer health risks. They are less likely to suffer from osteoporosis and to develop breast or ovarian cancer.

Promotes development

Breast-feeding strengthens the bond between a mother and her child. This direct physical contact provides the baby with warmth and security. At birth, snuggled up to his mother's breast, the baby is comforted by his first feeding, which helps to stabilize his body temperature. Breast-feeding fosters a baby's intellectual development. The longer he is breast-fed, at least until the age of 6 or 9 months, the greater the impact.

Economical and ecological

Breast milk is available at all times, free of charge. There is nothing to purchase and nothing to wash, prepare, store and warm up. The milk is always ready, day and night, and is available wherever you are. It is ecological, since it does not leave any waste such as empty containers, plastic, paper, metal, residues or polluting smoke generated by production or transportation.

Breast-feeding self-help groups

Breast-feeding self-help groups are made up of women who have breast-fed 1 or more children. Their knowledge is up-to-date and they offer support in a very simple, friendly manner. Most groups organize information sessions for new mothers to help prepare them for breast-feeding.

Find out about the services offered by groups in your area. Ask your hospital or CLSC how to reach them.

Production of breast milk

When it is stimulated regularly day and night, the mammary gland produces sufficient amounts of milk for baby.

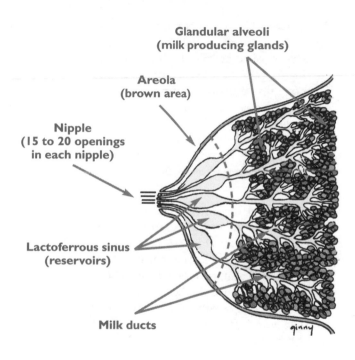

Glandular alveoli
(milk producing glands)

Areola
(brown area)

Nipple
(15 to 20 openings
in each nipple)

Lactoferrous sinus
(reservoirs)

Milk ducts

A hormonal change occurs at the time of childbirth. Prolactin increases, which in turn increases the production of colostrum, then milk. Your baby's sucking triggers the secretion of oxytocin, a hormone that provokes contractions of the glandular alveoli in the breast. This is the milk let-down reflex. This hormone is also responsible for the uterine contractions that are perceptible, especially during nursing the first days after birth and more intensely after the birth of a second child.

Initially, the milk **let-down reflex** can cause intense thirst. Some mothers also experience **painless** tingling in the breasts. Milk may flow spontaneously when the mother talks about her baby, hears the baby crying or as nursing time approaches. The let-down reflex can also occur several times during the same feeding session or so forcefully that the baby has to release the breast in order to catch his breath (see "Milk flow," page 183).

It is the baby's sucking that triggers milk production. When the baby properly latches on to the breast, milk is secreted abundantly (see "Latching on," page 163). The more your baby nurses, the more milk there is. Lactation adjusts to his appetite. For this reason, a baby must breast-feed according to his needs, without restricting either the number or duration of feedings. Remember that **numerous quality feedings** are a guarantee of successful breast-feeding.

Getting breast-feeding off to a good start

First feedings

In the hour following his birth, your baby will instinctively seek your breast, explore and discover the sucking reflex. Let your baby nurse as soon as possible, ideally within an hour of birth. If he does not nurse right away, hold him against your body until he wants to suckle. Your baby will smell you and recognize you, which will stimulate him.

The interval between the first and second feeding depends on the baby and how much milk he consumes. Some babies sleep for several consecutive hours after birth. Take advantage of this time to rest with your family, with baby near you. If your baby does not react right away, squeeze several drops of colostrum into his mouth. Is he still refusing to nurse? Do not insist. Offer him the breast later when he shows signs of being hungry. To stimulate the mammary gland, squeeze out a bit of milk from your breasts.

Hold your baby next to your skin. You will know when he is ready to nurse. Do not worry. Some babies are slower than others (see "Difficult nursing," page 181).

Latching on

The secret of successful breast-feeding is proper latching on. A baby who does not latch on properly sucks in vain as though he were trying to drink through an overly small straw. The breast may well be full but the baby is unable to empty it. Improper latching on can also injure the nipples. The situation can quickly become more complicated since a baby who does not latch on properly has trouble drinking efficiently. He may nurse for longer periods and aggravate injuries to the nipples.

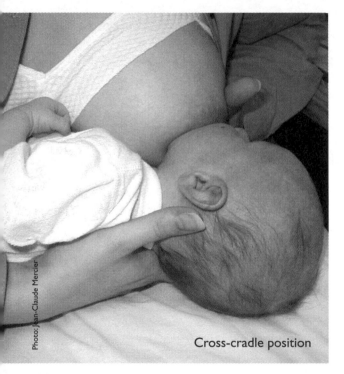

Photo: Jean-Claude Mercier

Cross-cradle position

At first, it is sometimes difficult to nurse the baby without assistance. Have confidence in yourself: with practice you and your baby will quickly become experts.

- Take the time to properly settle yourself. A comfortable chair, music, cushions or pillows and a glass of juice or milk will help you to relax. Make nursing a pleasant time.

- Do not wait until your baby cries before nursing him. He will be more patient (see "Signs of hunger," page 172).

- Choose a breast-feeding position that suits you. There are several positions such as the cradle, the cross-cradle, the football hold and the side-lying positions, but some basic principles apply to all of them. Regardless of the position you choose, your baby must be sufficiently turned toward you with his chest, tummy and thighs aligned. He must not have to turn his head in order to nurse.

- A self-help group can help you become familiar with the different positions.

Cross-cradle position

The cross-cradle position is one of the most frequently used by nursing mothers. It has 2 advantages. It allows the mother to properly support the baby's head and to see clearly how he latches on.

The baby rests on his mother's arm opposite the breast on which he is nursing. If you are nursing from the left breast, you will support your baby with your right arm. Place the palm of your right hand **under the nape of his neck**, not behind his head. Your fingers (except the thumb) support his head while your forearm supports his back and bottom. In this way, the baby's bottom is held between your thorax and forearm.

Hold your left breast with your left hand. Your thumb rests on the outer side of the breast and the other fingers on the inner side, far from the nipple and the areola, to form a U (see the photo on the next page).

Move your right arm to draw the baby closer so that his head is slightly tilted backward. His chin must touch your breast first and his nose should be opposite the nipple. The nipple will automatically point toward the baby's palate and not the back of his mouth.

Wait until your baby opens his mouth as though he were going to yawn. Wait until he is ready before nursing him.

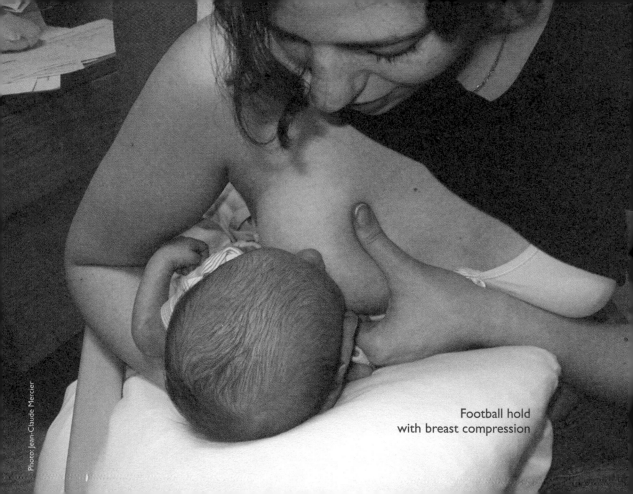

Football hold
with breast compression

Effective sucking

Regardless of the position you choose, whether you are seated or lying down, ensure that your baby latches on to the breast correctly.

- Make sure that he opens his mouth **wide**. To help him, you can brush his upper lip with the nipple, always pointed toward his palate. This gentle stimulation will encourage him

to seek the breast. Initially, this may take time. However, with practice, he will learn and the process will become simple.

- Make sure that your baby does not latch on to the nipple alone but also to a large part of areola (the brown area of the breast). His lower lip must cover a larger part of the areola than his upper lip (see photo, page 323).

The baby's first sucking motions are light and rapid. When the milk starts to flow, the sucking becomes slower and more sustained. The baby's jaw and ear usually move and you will hear him swallow the milk.

If your baby is breathing noisily, do not press on your breast with your finger to free up his nose. Instead, press his bottom against you, which should be sufficient to free up his nose. Do not worry. He does not risk suffocating. If he has trouble breathing, he will release the breast.

Pain is not normal. As soon as your nipples become painful, change the baby's position. First, use your index finger to gently lower his chin and curl up his lower lip in order to open his mouth wider. However, you may have to repeat the steps for latching on to the breast. Do you have questions? Consult someone trained in breast-feeding.

How to break the suction

If you must remove your baby from the breast, gently put your finger between his gums, in the corner of his mouth. This will break the suction and release the nipple.

Indicators of proper latching on

- Your baby's mouth is wide open when he latches on.

- The nipple is pointing toward the baby's palate.

- His chin is touching the breast.

- His mouth covers a large portion of the areola.

- His lips are curled outward.

- His tongue is under the nipple.

- You can hear him swallowing.

Before you go home

Normally, a nurse or someone skilled in breast-feeding should monitor you during the first feedings to ensure that the baby is latching on and sucking properly and that he is obtaining milk. The effectiveness of latching on and suction are more important than the number and duration of feedings in a 24-hour period. A baby who is sucking properly will not nurse for hours on end.

Have someone help you assess your baby's sucking. Make sure that you can recognize the signs that your baby is nursing properly and that he is obtaining milk.

Before you leave, ask someone to teach you the manual milk extraction technique (see page 198).

Have confidence in yourself. Your baby belongs to you and his parents you are primarily responsible for him. You have a say about the care that he receives. The team of caregivers is there to assist you in this uplifting experience for the entire family. Mothers are frequently easily moved to tears during this period. Take care of yourself and let others spoil you.

Coming home

Lactogenesis

Lactogenesis occurs between the third and fifth day after birth. It lasts between 12 and 48 hours. The breasts increase in size, stretch and swell, and become sensitive.

▶ What to do

Early (from the time of birth), regular (day and night, wherever you are) and frequent (from 8 to 12 times in a 24-hour period) nursing will help soothe the discomfort. Most babies spontaneously want to nurse more frequently at this stage, which often helps to relieve the breasts. To promote the flow of milk, apply hot compresses to your breasts a minute or two before nursing and squeeze out a bit of milk. If your baby does not sufficiently empty out the breast, it may be useful to express additional milk after nursing.

Are your breasts really painful? To reduce swelling and pain, apply a bag of crushed ice, a bag of frozen vegetables or an ice pack wrapped in a towel for roughly 15 minutes. Since cold reduces milk flow, place hot compresses on the breasts two minutes before your baby nurses.

Acetaminophen, for example, Atasol or Tylenol, taken 20 to 30 minutes before nursing is effective and and not dangerous for the baby. Rest. Lactogenesis is a part of the natural lactation process and the discomfort it causes lasts for roughly 25 to 36 hours.

Nursing schedule

After 2 or 3 days, a newborn is less drowsy and more clearly indicates his needs.

Learn to recognize feeding cues and signs of hunger (see "Signs of hunger," page 172). It is the frequency and quality of feedings that allow your baby to consume sufficient milk. Usually, he drinks 8 to 12 times in a 24-hour period. This cycle includes a period of sleep that is longer than the others, although not necessarily at night.

Some babies nurse more frequently at certain times of the day and less frequently at other times. This is normal.

Do not expect your baby to sleep through the night as soon as he comes home from the hospital. The age at which a child sleeps for 6 consecutive hours depends on his biological rhythm and his environment. It varies considerably from one child to the next but does not usually occur until the child is several months old.

Duration of nursing

There is no such thing as a "normal" nursing. Some babies drink little during a feeding but nurse often, while other infants drink a lot but nurse less often. This depends on the baby's sucking, his appetite and temperament, and on the flow of milk from the mammary gland. What is important is that your baby latches on properly (see "Indicators of proper latching on," page 168), nurses efficiently and **swallows** the milk (see "Effective sucking," page 167).

Feeding a newborn, that is, nursing, burping the baby and changing his diaper, may take from 45 to 90 minutes. Feedings usually last from 5 to 30 minutes per breast, but they tend to grow shorter as the baby grows.

Let your baby nurse until he stops of his own accord or he starts to fall asleep. **Do not look at your watch but at your baby.** Timing your baby's feedings does not prevent injuries to the nipples and may deprive your baby of some of the milk he needs.

One or two breasts?

Let your baby nurse from the first breast until he is full, burp him, then offer him the other breast, which he will take if he is hungry. Sometimes he will take only 1 breast, sometimes both. Follow his pace. Start the next feeding with the breast offered last, whether or not your baby nursed and if you are unsure, offer the breast that seems heaviest to you.

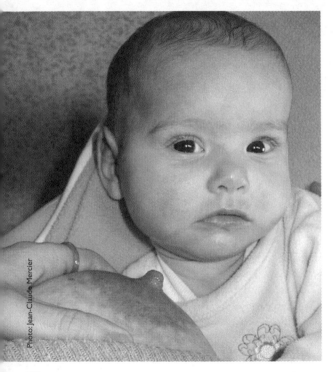

Photo: Jean-Claude Mercier

Handy hint

If you are afraid that you will forget from which breast the baby nursed last, put a safety pin or ribbon on the appropriate side of your bra to remind you.

Signs of hunger

Long before he starts crying a baby shows that he wants to nurse. His breathing changes and his eyes, mouth or face move. Next, he moves his arms and legs, stretches and brings his hands up to his mouth or face. Sucking motions follow.

All of these indicators tell you that your baby is hungry. Do not wait for him to cry before feeding. He could get tired and might refuse to nurse even if he is famished.

Drowsy or impatient baby

During the first 3 to 6 weeks, babies tend to fall asleep while nursing when milk flow slows down **even when they have not had enough milk**. After this period, they may become fidgety if the flow of milk is limited. Infants barely a few days old may become agitated when they do not get the milk quickly enough.

If your baby falls asleep, you must stimulate him by tickling him, holding him against your body, talking to him or singing to him. Check that he is latching on properly (see "Indicators of proper latching on," page 168). You can encourage him to nurse by using the breast compression technique.

Breast compression technique

This technique is useful when the baby:

- quickly falls asleep while nursing;
- does not gain enough weight;
- wants to nurse frequently or for a long time.

It is especially advisable during the first days of the baby's life to help him drink colostrum.

It is preferable to use the cross-cradle position (see "Cross-cradle position," page 165). Cup the breast with the hand, the thumb on one side and the fingers on the other, and squeeze the breast. Make sure that you keep the fingers far from the areola **without shifting them**. The movement **must not be painful or stretch the areola**.

The compression increases the flow of milk and your baby will become more active and will once again nurse effectively. Maintain the pressure for as long as he continues to swallow milk. As soon as he stops nursing, release the breast. Repeat the process until he stops swallowing. If your baby seems to want it, give him the other breast in the same way. You can then return to the first breast and even the second one, if need be.

When your baby is nursing better, you can abandon the compression technique. It is unnecessary when nursing is going well.

Breast size

The appearance and texture of the breasts is largely a question of heredity. The breasts change, like the rest of the body, during a woman's lifetime. Nursing does not deform the breasts, which will grow larger, then smaller. Once the baby has been weaned, they will gradually return to their normal shape.

During the first 6 weeks of breast-feeding, the breasts usually swell. Toward the second month, they become softer to the touch and diminish in size. Do not worry. You are secreting **more milk** than before and the mammary gland has adjusted to nursing.

Care of the breasts

A daily shower or bath is sufficient to keep your breasts clean. Creams, ointments and other products are not advisable. You can leave a few drops of milk on the nipples after your baby has nursed.

There is no point in washing your breasts before each feeding. Doing so may even irritate them. However, do wash your hands with soap and water. This is the best way to prevent infections.

Avoid moisture. If you use breast-feeding pads, choose cotton or paper pads without a plastic lining and change them often.

Do not hesitate to sleep with your breasts bare if you feel at ease doing so.

Whether or not you wear a bra depends on your comfort. If you wear a bra, it is best to choose a comfortable nursing bra with ample cups that do not constrict your breasts.

Nursing in public

More and more mothers are nursing in public. Find a quiet, comfortable spot. It is essential that you feel at ease. If you breast-feed with confidence and modesty, others will accept you. A big, soft sweater will make things easier. Some public places provide space for breast-feeding and baby care. Find out about them.

Photo: Health Canada

Keep your baby nearby

Keeping your baby near you helps you to get to know him better and to identify his needs. During the first months of his life, it is recommended that the baby remain in the same room as his parents (see "Crib death," page 62. To facilitate breast-feeding, you can install your baby's bed in your room (see "Your baby's bed," page 351).

You can safely nurse your baby lying down provided that you follow the recommendations indicated below.

- The mattress must be firm. Avoid at all costs water beds, overly soft mattresses and stuffed furniture such as sofas.

- It is important to inform anyone sharing the bed in which the baby nurses of the baby's presence in the bed.

- Never let a baby sleep alone in an adult's bed.

Pacifiers and bottles

Avoid pacifiers. Some babies can have trouble nursing or even reject the breast after being given a pacifier, which can lead to a drop in the quantity of milk. A good feeding is a better way to console your baby. Direct contact with his father's skin is also soothing.

Avoid giving your newborn anything but breast milk. Additional water, sugar water or infant formula is rarely necessary when a healthy full-term baby is breast-feeding properly. If it is necessary to give your baby breast milk (or, failing that, a substitute) other than through breast-feeding, the use of a cup seems a better choice than a bottle. Different approaches can be used to facilitate continued breast-feeding. Contact a CLSC nurse, a breast-feeding consultant or a breast-feeding self-help group.

A difficult hurdle

A difficult hurdle often arises between the fourth and sixth weeks, especially for first-time mothers. During this period, the baby experiences a growth spurt and wants to nurse frequently. He may even want to nurse every hour, which becomes exhausting. The situation should get back to normal within 24 or 48 hours since milk production will adjust to the baby's needs.

Doubting your ability to continue? Are you thinking of weaning your baby? Do not remain isolated. Talk to your partner, a friend or a breast-feeding specialist. Get out of the house and meet your friends. Humour and laughter are good medicine.

Breast-feeding self-help groups or support groups for new mothers organize meetings that may help (see "Useful addresses," page 442).

Is your baby getting enough milk?

There are several ways to tell whether your baby is getting enough milk.

- After the first week of your baby's life, his urine is clear and odourless. He thoroughly wets at least 5 or 6 diapers a day. His stools are liquid or very soft and frequent, that is, from 2 to 5 a day for the first 4 weeks, then less frequent (for example, 1 stool every 3 to 7 days), although abundant (see figure, page 207).

- His weight increases sufficiently and steadily (see "How baby grows," page 317).

Off to a Good Start in Life

A good diet from birth will help your child grow up healthy and strong. For further information on the benefits of breast-feeding or advice about the importance of a wholesome, varied diet, consult a dietitian/nutritionist.

- He sleeps well and wakes up on his own.
- He displays signs of hunger such as salivating, sucking on his fist and chewing.

What should you do if your baby is not drinking enough?

- Make sure that your baby is nursing properly. Check (or have someone else check) to see that he is latching on properly.
- Breast-feed your baby more often. Wake the baby up if need be.
- Keep your baby in contact with your skin to calm him and stimulate him to drink more often.
- Use the breast compression technique (see page 173).
- At each feeding, let the baby nurse from both breasts.

- Extract milk between feedings to increase milk production. Offer the baby this milk after the next feeding, preferably in a cup. Avoid using a baby bottle (see "Pacifiers and bottles," page 176).
- Avoid a nipple shield since it reduces milk production.

Consider external factors such as the consumption of contraceptive pills that might hamper lactation. Rest.

Think of yourself

Breast-feeding also means adopting the pace of your baby's life. Be sure to regularly take advantage of the simple joys that this period of your life affords you. Slow down. Put aside unessential tasks and put off the baby reception.

Know when to ask for help and accept the help that is offered.

Think of yourself. Allow yourself moments of respite and quiet to catch up on the sleep that you will inevitably lose. Eat sufficient amounts at meals and allow yourself the pleasure of a healthy snack, if need be. Relax. Get out in the sun and fresh air, with or without your baby. You can get a babysitter. Laugh and cry if that is what you feel like doing. Whether or not they are breast-feeding, some mothers are subject to crying spells after giving birth. If crying makes you feel better, then let yourself go.

An important reminder

Proper latching on is essential for successful breast-feeding.

12 tips to facilitate breast-feeding

1. Let your baby nurse as soon as possible, ideally within an hour of birth.

2. Keep your baby near you day and night. He can sleep with you if you want.

3. Remember that your milk is perfectly suited to your newborn. It is nourishing, rich and will help him put on weight. It is a wonderful natural gift.

4. Breast-feed your baby on demand, when he is hungry. Frequent nursing stimulates milk production.

5. Learn to recognize your baby's hunger signs.

6. Make sure that your baby is breathing properly, correctly latches on to the breast, is sucking efficiently and obtaining the milk he needs.

7. To avoid hampering lactation, do not skip feedings, offer your baby a pacifier or give him another kind of milk before the age of 4 weeks.

8. If possible, wait until your baby is 6 months old before giving him another kind of milk or solid food. In this way, he will benefit fully from breast milk.

9. Try not to worry. As soon as you feel worried or uneasy, contact the CLSC nurse, a breast-feeding self-help group in your area or a breast-feeding clinic.

10. Slow down. Breast-feeding an infant means adopting a newborn's pace. Put aside unimportant tasks and get help with essential ones.

11. Think of yourself. Allow yourself moments of respite and quiet to catch up on the sleep that you will inevitably lose.

12. Have confidence in yourself!

Breast-feeding problems and solutions

After the first few weeks, most mothers do not experience any problems. However, problems can arise.

Difficult nursing

Some babies recover less quickly than others from the strain of birth and are less skilful at latching on to the breast. If this is the case with your child, try to feed him regularly. Hold him frequently with his skin against yours to stimulate his interest in the breast and to reassure him. Request help in extracting your colostrum and give it to your baby with a dropper, a cup or a small breast tube. Avoid using a baby bottle.

If your breasts are swollen, your baby may find it hard to nurse (see "Engorgement," page 188). **Do not force your baby to take the breast** as he could develop an aversion to it.

If your baby has taken a bottle or pacifier, you may need help during the first days and during lactogenesis. Sucking the breast is different from sucking a baby bottle.

▶ **What to do**

It is important to keep your baby hydrated. If he has difficulty nursing and does not often wet his diaper, immediately request help (see "Is your baby getting enough milk?" page 177). Seek the cause of the problem and you will find a solution. Stay calm and confident.

Refusal to nurse

An older infant may refuse the breast for no apparent reason. He is calm, is gaining weight well, is not sick but does not want to nurse. Your baby is on strike!

▶ What to do

Do not force your baby to nurse. Be patient, since this situation should not last long. A baby will often take the breast if you offer it while he is sleeping.

Sleepy baby

Your baby sleeps a lot and nurses fewer than 8 times a day. If he is gaining weight steadily, there is nothing to fear. However, if he is gaining weight slowly, you must stimulate him.

▶ What to do

Caress your baby and pat him gently. Hold him with his skin against yours and frequently offer him the breast (at least 8 to 12 times every 24 hours). Wake him up, if need be. Watch for signs of light sleep (sucking motion, eye movement under his eyelids, and so on). It will be easier to wake him up then. Use the breast compression technique (see "Breast compression technique," page 173). Watch your baby for signs of satisfaction (see "Is your baby getting enough milk?" page 177).

Promptly consult your doctor if your baby is losing weight.

Little milk

Frequent crying, lengthy or frequent feedings and slow weight gain may lead the mother to believe that she is not producing enough milk. This is not necessarily true (see "Indicators of proper latching on," page 168). Is your baby crying? Remember that infants cry for reasons that often have nothing to do with a shortage of milk (see "Temperament," page 72).

Is your baby nursing more often than you expected? This means that he is getting milk. Remember that breast milk is digested quickly. During periods of rapid growth, your baby must nurse more often to stimulate lactation (see "Hunger pangs," page 322).

▶ What to do

If your baby nurses for a very long time, make sure that he is latching on to the breast properly. If he sucks the breast more effectively he may obtain more milk in less time. However, if after sucking actively he only swallows after every 4 or 5 sucking movements and starts to fall asleep, then he is no longer really hungry.

Do not be influenced by others. Before you believe anyone who says that you do not have enough milk or that your milk is too skimpy, take the time to assess the situation.

Milk flow

During the first few weeks, your breasts may leak between feedings or at night. This is normal and does not mean that you have too much milk. The situation will correct itself within a few days. For your own comfort, put a towel on the bed at night to absorb the leakage.

Your baby is gaining weight steadily and frequently wetting his diapers but often chokes while nursing, especially at the beginning. He may also start crying and release the breast when milk runs over his face. The flow of milk in your breast is probably very strong.

▶ What to do

Reduce the pressure by extracting a bit of milk before the feeding. Pause when your baby starts to choke. Take advantage of the opportunity to burp him. Try to give him only one breast per feeding, which will help you regulate the flow of milk. You can also vary the feeding position.

Short nipples

Most babies get used to them. When babies latch on to the breast properly, they take the areola and the nipple. However, your baby may get impatient.

▶ What to do

If your baby gets agitated, withdraw the breast for several minutes until he calms down. To prevent this situation, nurse your baby before he becomes famished. If need be, first give him a bit of breast milk in a spoon or cup to calm him. Avoid baby bottles, pacifiers and nipple shields.

Painful nipples

Breast-feeding is a pleasant experience and should not be painful. The nipples are frequently sensitive the first week, above all at the beginning of a feeding. Baby and mother are both learning. After this period, breast-feeding should be trouble-free. You must investigate any pain that persists after the first minute of feeding or that makes you fearful of nursing. The main cause is probably improper latching on to the breast. This situation can cause chapping and cracking of the nipple. The baby may nurse inefficiently, experience insufficient weight gain, and cry.

▶ What to do

Immediately request assistance from a breast-feeding specialist. It is easier to remedy the problem when it first appears.

Chapping and cracking

The nipple and areola become redder, then chapping and cracking appear. While they are not dangerous for the baby, they quickly become painful for the mother. The pain is particularly intense at the beginning of nursing and can continue throughout breast-feeding. The way the baby latches on to the breast is probably the cause.

▶ What to do

Persistent pain or chapping is a leading cause of premature weaning. **Regardless of what people tell you, pain is not normal**. Do not suffer in silence. **Check (or have someone else check) the baby's latching on and suction**. Once the cause of the injury is remedied, the pain will diminish quickly. Start the feeding with the least sensitive breast. Vary your breast-feeding position.

At the end of the feeding, put several drops of breast milk on the nipple. Keep the nipples dry and, if need be, the breasts bare. Ointments and creams sold over the counter are not advisable because they do not remedy the problem. An analgesic such as acetaminophen (e.g. Atasol, Tylenol) can also help. Avoid a nipple shield, which could aggravate the problem.

Thrush (fungal infection)

Sudden, unexplained pain during nursing when everything was previously going well may stem from a fungal infection. However, the pain may occur gradually, not abruptly, or occur at the same time as an existing pain. It may be confined to the nipple and the areola, but it may also be felt as a burning sensation inside the breast. It tends to increase during feeding and persist afterward while in other cases (see "Chapping Cracking," page 185) it diminishes gradually.

The areola and nipple are frequently red and sensitive but may appear normal. Cracks are the ideal site for a fungal infection that is often associated with thrush in children.

However, you can suffer from a fungal infection even if your baby does not have thrush in his mouth. Antibiotics consumed by the mother make the baby more sensitive to infection.

▶ What to do

Both mother and baby must be treated. Gentian violet is a good remedy and is sold over the counter: 15 mL (1 tablespoon) of a 0.5% to 1% **aqueous** solution is sufficient for the entire treatment. It is applied once a day in conjunction with a nystatin cream such as Nilstat or Nyaderm or a miconazole cream, such as Micatin or Monistat Derm. Gentian violet treats the mother and baby simultaneously.

Application:

- Swab the baby's mouth with a cotton swab dipped in gentian violet.

- Give the baby both breasts in order to colour them.

- Add gentian violet to the breasts if they are not completely coloured.

Apply a thin layer of ointment to the nipples after the other feedings. It is not necessary to remove it between feedings.

After 4 days, stop the treatment with gentian violet if the pain has disappeared or if there is no improvement, but continue to apply the cream for a few days. If it has not completely improved, continue the treatment with gentian violet for not more than 3 days. After 7 days, stop the treatment, regardless of the result. See your doctor. An oral treatment may be helpful.

Be careful, gentian stains clothing and bedding. Apply the treatment preferably at bedtime. You can give your baby milk extracted during the treatment period, but do not freeze the milk as there is a risk of new infection.

An important reminder

- Check how your baby latches on to the breast (see "Latching on," page 163).
- Wash reusable compresses in hot water and discard the others (see also "Thrush in the mouth," page 395).

Irritated skin

Eczema or contact dermatitis may appear on the nipples and areolas. The skin is pink or clearly red and hot.

▶ What to do

If you are already putting a cream, lotion, lanolin or other product on your breasts, stop the applications. However, a prescription medicated ointment may be necessary. Promptly consult your doctor.

Engorgement (plugged lactiferous duct)

When the lactiferous duct is plugged, milk in this duct no longer flows from the nipple. If you feel the breast after your baby has nursed, you find a small, hard lump that is painful to the touch, occasionally accompanied by redness. There are several possible causes for the obstruction: the breast has been full too long, has been pinched by the bra or infant carrier, or is reacting to fatigue. The discomfort is confined to the breast (usually only one) and the mother does not feel sick. However, if the milk is plugged for too long, an infection may occur.

▶ What to do

Avoid anything that pinches the breast. Apply moist heat to the entire breast in the bath or shower or using compresses while gently massaging the affected area toward the nipple.

Nurse your baby frequently (8 to 12 times a day) starting with the affected breast and using a variety of positions in order to facilitate the flow of milk. If possible, make sure that your baby's chin or nose points toward the lump when he is nursing. Gently rub the affected area during nursing. Take a hot bath before nursing.

Avoid wearing an overly tight bra. Rest. Keep your baby in bed with you if you want. Acetaminophen, for example, Atasol or Tylenol, can soothe the pain.

If the lump persists after 24 hours of treatment, consult a breast-feeding specialist.

Milk blister

A small blister forms on the nipple. It often causes intense pain in the entire breast, especially at the end of a feeding.

▶ What to do

Gently press on the blister, whose contents often have the consistency of toothpaste, and attempt to burst it. Massage the breast while taking a long, hot bath. If you nurse your baby right after your bath, he may succeed in unplugging the nipple.

Mastitis

Mastitis is a bacterial infection of the breast that is often caused by milk retention. It is painful but is not dangerous for the mother or baby. Breast-feeding allows for more rapid recovery since the breast empties quickly. **Your breast milk is still good**.

The exact cause of mastitis is unknown. However, poor drainage of the breasts or cracking promote it. At all times, make sure that your baby latches on to the breast properly and avoid prolonged engorgement (see "Engorgement," page 188). Moreover, mastitis often occurs when the mother is overworked. Try to eliminate certain tasks and rest more often with your baby.

The breast has a hardened, red, swollen, painful area. The mother is aching all over, shivering and exhausted. She is usually (although not always) feverish, with a temperature of over 38.3°C (101°F). She feels sick.

▶ What to do

You must decompress the engorged breast. Remove your bra and rest in bed. Apply hot compresses. If need be, keep your baby in bed with you. Nurse him very often on the painful breast, even at night. If nursing is very uncomfortable for you, first give your baby the other breast. Change breasts as soon as milk flows spontaneously from the painful breast. Vary the baby's position during the feeding. If your baby has not nursed on the affected breast, extract the milk. The breast must become supple. Acetaminophen, for example, Atasol or Tylenol, can soothe the pain and fever. Eat properly and drink plenty of fluids.

If the symptoms begin to diminish within 12 hours, an antibiotic will probably not be necessary. If it takes longer, an antibiotic might be required. Whether or not you take an antibiotic, the situation must improve steadily. A sudden aggravation of the condition or an interruption in improvement for more than 24 hours requires that you consult your doctor.

It will take between 2 and 5 days for mastitis to clear up. The fever usually disappears within 24 hours, the pain in less than 48 hours and the hardened area within a few days. Redness can persist for a week or more.

An important reminder

If fever has persisted for 24 hours or rises rapidly, consult your doctor. If you have to take antibiotics, do so during the prescribed time, usually 10 days, to avoid a relapse. Effective antibiotics are available that do not pose any risk during breast-feeding. Discuss the matter with your doctor. Above all, continue to breast-feed and rest.

Abscess

In rare cases, mastitis can degenerate into an abscess. Despite treatment, a painful lump persists.

▶ **What to do**

See your doctor. A breast-feeding consultant or someone from a self-help group can suggest practical solutions that help you continue breast-feeding.

Specific situations

Caesarean section

Was your baby born by Caesarean section? There is nothing to prevent you from breast-feeding him. If you were under general anaesthesia, you can breast-feed as soon as you are fully awake and feel comfortable. If you received epidural anaesthesia (injected into the lower back), you can breast-feed as soon as possible, ideally within an hour of your baby's birth, even if you are still under the effect of the epidural anaesthesia. Some hospitals encourage the mother to first nurse the baby in the operating room or the recovery room.

The presence of your partner or another important person will enable you to keep your baby in your room. Hospital staff should be available to help you give the baby the breast. You will soon be able to care for your baby yourself.

Premature babies

Even if your baby is born before the 37th week of pregnancy, you can breast-feed him. Mother's milk is the best milk for him because its composition adapts to his needs. **You alone can offer him this precious food.**

Depending on the number of weeks your baby spent in the womb, you will perhaps need a bit of extra patience and perseverance. As long as your baby is in the hospital, you must maintain milk production by extracting it every 3 or 4 hours during the day and, if possible, at night, using an electric breast pump. **Thinking about your baby will stimulate the let-down reflex** (see "Extraction and storage of breast milk," page 198). When you visit your baby in the neonatology department and his condition allows it, hold him often and for a long time in your arms with his skin against yours. He will get used to you and will find it easier to take the breast when the time comes. Such contact has been shown to benefit both the baby and his parents. It is just as precious as the food that your infant receives.

Initially, the nurses will give your baby your milk using a very thin tube. As soon as your baby can nurse, you can give him the breast. He will perhaps need food supplements while he is in the hospital, but as soon as he comes home, your milk will provide all the nourishment he needs.

Be patient. Premature babies need time to learn to breast-feed. The Association des parents d'enfants prématurés du Québec can offer you support (see "APEP," page 442).

Twins

You can breast-feed twins. The more you stimulate the mammary gland, the more milk you will produce. However, feeding two infants at the same time is demanding. Put aside unessential tasks and seek help from your loved ones with domestic chores such as laundry, cooking and shopping. Rest.

It is preferable to feed both babies breast milk alone. However, you can alternate between mother's milk and infant formula.

A self-help group can put you in touch with a mother who has had the same experience.

Breast surgery

Breast augmentation does not usually pose a problem.

Breast reduction is more damaging to the breast. It is possible to breast-feed in this case, but some mothers will also have to give their infants formula.

To ensure successful breast-feeding, consult a self-help group to properly prepare yourself, even before your baby is born.

Resumption of lactation

If you did not breast-feed your baby at birth or if he is allergic to infant formula, can you breast-feed him?

It is not too late. With determination and assistance, you can restore lactation after weaning even if you have never breast-fed your baby.

Breast-feeding an adopted baby is also possible.

Alcohol and tobacco

Some of the alcohol a mother consumes ends up in her breast milk. For this reason, it is preferable to limit consumption. Avoid consuming alcohol regularly. However, wine and beer consumed occasionally in small amounts do not appear to be harmful to your baby.

As is true during pregnancy, tobacco is harmful to you and your baby (see "Beware of tobacco smoke," page 348). It can hamper milk production and may cause crying, irritability and insomnia in children. **However, the benefits of mother's milk are sufficiently important for you to breast-feed despite everything.** If you cannot manage without a cigarette, smoke outside the home, well away from your baby. Try to avoid smoking just before nursing. Nicotine patches are compatible with breast-feeding.

Marijuana and other drugs

Can an occasional joint harm a breast-fed baby? While the long-term effects of marijuana on a baby are unknown, we do know that it enters breast milk. Avoid even occasional consumption, which is not recommended. Regular consumption of marijuana is obviously prohibited.

As for other drugs such as amphetamines, cocaine, heroin, LSD and PCP, they are unquestionably dangerous for your baby. They are incompatible with breast-feeding and your role as parents.

Medication

Most medications turn up in breast milk, although in very small amounts. Mothers whose doctors advise them to stop breast-feeding in order to take medication must make sure that the doctor's recommendation is based on reliable sources or ask him to prescribe another medicine that is compatible with breast-feeding. It is usually easy to find another medication to treat the most common illnesses. It is very rarely necessary to interrupt breast-feeding for the duration of the treatment.

Do not take any medication or natural products, which are sometimes highly active, without consulting a health professional (see page 314). Limit yourself to medication that is absolutely essential.

Breast-feeding and working

Some mothers continue to breast-feed when they return to work. Day care services in the workplace are becoming more widespread and are enabling mothers to nurse their babies on site. If such a service is not available where you work, you can extract your milk and refrigerate or freeze it. Someone else can give it to your baby. You can thus continue to offer your baby the food best suited to his development and health.

Moreover, **you can opt for mixed feeding**, that is breast-feed your baby when you are at home and feed him formula when you are absent or at work. Your milk production will adapt to this type of breast-feeding routine, which can continue until the child is 1 year of age or older.

If your baby is over 6 months of age, he does not necessarily need a baby bottle. Like all other babies at this age, he is starting to eat solid food with a spoon and learning to drink out of a cup, which can satisfy his hunger. However, your baby may want to nurse more often in the evening or even at night.

A breast-feeding self-help group can help you explore different possibilities and offer support in carrying them out.

Dangerous working conditions

In the workplace, you may take advantage of preventive reassignment if you are exposed to certain contaminants such as solvents, ink and dyes that can be harmful while you are breast-feeding. Consult your doctor.

Extraction and storage of breast milk

It is often useful to extract breast milk. Extraction allows the mother to soothe an engorged breast. The baby can drink his mother's milk even when she is absent. In the event of prolonged separation, when the baby is premature or has to be hospitalized, extraction makes it possible to maintain lactation.

Extracting milk

There are several ways to extract breast milk. With experience, you will find the method that suits you best. Always handle the breasts gently.

The ideal time to extract milk is immediately after nursing your baby since the let-down reflex has already been initiated. If your baby has only nursed from one breast, it will be easier to empty the other breast. However, if it suits you better, you can choose some other time when you are not too rushed. Be sure to take time to relax and rest before you start.

Initially, spend only 5 to 10 minutes per breast. Lengthen the sessions as the amount of milk increases. It is normal to obtain only a few drops of milk when you begin extraction. **Be patient.**

Manual extraction

- Thoroughly wash your hands to avoid contamination.

- Put a big, deep, thoroughly washed and rinsed bowl on a clean surface near you.

- Seat yourself comfortably and lean forward so that your breast hangs above the bowl.

Manual Expression

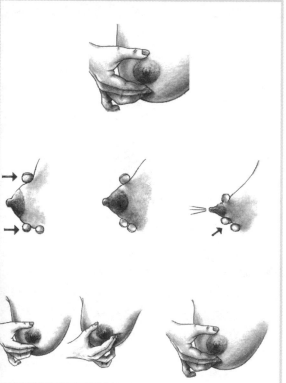

See description on page 198

See description on page 198

If nature needs little help!

For Suggested Pump	Harmony™	MiniElectric™	Pump In Style®	Symphony™
A missed feeding	•	•		
An evening out from baby	•	•		
Working part-time	•	•		
Occasional use, few times per week	•	•		
Working full-time			•	•
Premature or hospitalized baby				•
Low milk supply				•
Sore nipples or engorgement			•	•
Latch-on problems or breast infection			•	•
Drawing out flat or inverted nipples	•	•	•	•

° Good   • Better   • Best

Symphony™

Harmony™

MiniElectric™

Medela also offers:

- Specialty Feeding Products

- Baby Scales

- Maternity/Nursing Intimate Apparel

To locate Medela products in your area or to get more information please call: 1-800-435-8316

www.medela.ca

 medela

- To facilitate the let-down reflex, you can gently massage your breast using a circular motion or by gently caressing it from the base of the nipple and gently rub the nipple with the palm of your hand.

- Put the thumb and index finger at the edge of the areola. The motion has 2 steps. **Do not slide or move the fingers on the skin**:

  1. press the breast by pushing towards the ribs;
  2. draw the thumb and index finger closer together in a pinching movement.

  It is not necessary to press hard. The movement must not leave a mark on the breast or be painful. It will take a bit of practice to properly position your fingers.

- Repeat the movement several times. It reproduces suction by the baby when he squeezes the breast with his tongue. At first, the milk will flow a drop at a time and then will become a stream.

- Work your way around the breast by moving the fingers in order to entirely empty the breast.

Before you leave the hospital, a nurse, a physician or a midwife should show you how to extract milk manually. If you need help, consult a breast-feeding self-help group.

Do not worry. The technique is easy to learn. It is easier to do it than to describe it.

Electric breast pump

Electric breast pumps are efficient and very practical when the mother must extract her milk for a long period of time. You can rent breast pumps. Do not hesitate to contact a breast-feeding self-help group or your CLSC.

▣ Handy hint

To stimulate the let-down reflex, think about your baby or look at a photo of him.

Storing breast milk

Mother's milk is best when drunk fresh from the breast. However, it refrigerates and freezes well.

Keep it at room temperature if it is to be consumed within 4 to 8 hours of being extracted. If it is to be consumed within a few days, refrigerate it instead of freezing it. If it will not be consumed for 5 days or more, freeze it at once.

	ROOM TEMPERATURE	REFRIGERATOR	FREEZER
Fresh breast milk	4 hours at 25°C (77°F) 8 hours at 19 to 22°C (66.2-71.6°F)	3 to 5 days at 4°C (39.2°F)	3 to 4 months (refrigerator freezer) 6 months (chest freezer)
Thawed breast milk	1 hour	24 hours	Do not refreeze

An important reminder

- The limits on storage are not cumulative. Do not store the milk for 8 hours at room temperature, then refrigerate it for 5 days, and then freeze it.

- The limits do not apply to milk intended for a premature baby who is still in the hospital. Follow the advice of hospital staff.

- Rigorous hygiene is essential. Wash your hands and make sure that the containers are clean.

Depending on the mother's diet, breast milk is bluish, yellowish or brownish white. This is normal. Since it is not homogenized, the fat separates from the rest. Simply shake it before using.

Choice of containers

You can store the milk in glass or rigid plastic baby bottles or even in thick freezer bags designed for mother's milk. Ordinary bags are too thin for freezing. Use 2 as they are fragile.

It is practical to have several small portions of breast milk on hand. Avoid containers that are too big.

If you are storing your milk for a hospitalized, premature or sick baby, follow the advice of hospital staff.

Freezing

Place all of the containers of frozen milk in a storage container with a solid cover. Prolonged freezing slightly reduces the nutritional value of mother's milk. However, its qualities are superior to any other type of milk.

- Pour the milk into the container of your choice but do not fill it full. The milk will expand as it freezes.

- Write the date on the properly closed container.

- Put the container in the refrigerator to cool.

- Once it has cooled, store it in the freezer in the storage container for breast milk.

- Use the oldest milk first.

How to warm up breast milk

Do not heat breast milk in the microwave oven since it loses most of the antibodies that protect your baby from several diseases of the digestive system and respiratory tract.

If you have just taken the milk out of the refrigerator, run hot tap water over the bag or set it in hot water until it is warm. Shake well, check the temperature and give it to your baby.

If you have just taken the milk out of the freezer, run cold tap water over the frozen container. Gradually add hot tap water until the milk is warm. Or, you can leave the frozen milk in the refrigerator for 10 to 12 hours, then warm it up with hot water. Shake well, check the temperature and give it to your baby.

Weaning

As is true of other stages in a child's development, weaning varies from one child to the next. It occurs early for some children and late for others. Whether the mother or the child initiates weaning depends on factors such as the child's age and temperament, the mother's feelings on the matter, and the approach adopted.

Take the time that you need to decide. Be attentive to your child and remain flexible. If possible, postpone weaning a sick child. He needs his mother's milk and the comforting contact that breast-feeding provides.

At the age of 9 months, your child can drink 3.25% homogenized milk instead of breast milk. Before that age, it is better to feed him iron-enriched infant formula.

Gradual weaning

Gradual weaning spread over more than four weeks is recommended. It will help the mother avoid engorgement and, at the same time, give the baby a chance to get used to this new way of drinking.

Start by replacing 1 feeding, for example, in the afternoon, with the new milk in a baby bottle, cup or glass. Between feedings, you can soothe your breasts by extracting a bit of milk or simply let the milk leak out under a hot shower.

After several days, when you no longer feel discomfort in the breasts, replace another feeding with the new milk, and so on. However, do not skip 2 consecutive feedings. Some mothers maintain the evening and morning feedings for a longer period of time. Be flexible and adjust to your child's pace.

Abrupt weaning

Abrupt weaning is not recommended since it can be painful for the mother and baby. If you are briefly separated from your baby you do not necessarily have to wean him. It is possible to maintain milk production during the separation and resume breast-feeding when you return. Consult a self-help group for assistance.

If you have to abruptly wean your baby:

- extract a bit of milk from your breasts to reduce swelling. You will need to extract milk less and less frequently;

- examine your breasts and monitor them to prevent problems such as engorgement, plugged ducts or mastitis, which can occur in subsequent weeks.

Transition to a bottle or cup

Drinking from a bottle or cup is a new experience for your child. If he protests, do not be put off by his refusal. **Stay calm and confident. He will get used to it.**

Your child may only accept a baby bottle after 1 or 2 weeks of effort. Entrust bottle-feeding to someone else, for example the child's father, to facilitate the transition. Be perseverant. Learning to drink from a bottle is a new skil! for your baby.

From the age of 6 months a child can start drinking from a cup. At first, he will drink only a small amount of milk. This is normal. Give him additional milk from the bottle. Make sure that your child is drinking enough milk, which continues to be the basic food during his first year of life. It provides the calcium and proteins that he needs to grow.

To facilitate the transition

- Without refusing to give your child the breast, you may decide not to offer it to him.

- Delay feedings if your child is not too impatient. This will help space them and reduce the number of feedings.

- Shorten the feedings.

- Change your daily habits. For example, do not sit in the chair where you normally breast-feed, which the child associates with nursing.

- Ask the father to participate. Discretely withdraw at the child's meal times.

- If your child is over 9 months of age, offer him a snack before his usual nursing time.

- Start the change when your child is in good health and not too hungry.

- First give your baby breast milk in a bottle or cup, then the new milk.

- Do not give the bottle or cup in the same way as the breast. Place your baby in front of you and give him the bottle or cup. Talk to him and smile.

- **Remember that you can change your mind during weaning and resume breast-feeding**. Consult a self-help group.

Breastfeeding Your Baby

GUIDELINES FOR NURSING MOTHERS

R BABY'S AGE	1 DAY	2 DAYS	3 DAYS	WEEK 1 4 DAYS	5 DAYS	6 DAYS	7 DAYS	2 WEEKS	3 WEEKS	4 WEEKS	5 WEEKS	6 WEEKS to 6 MONTHS
Baby's Tummy Size	Size of a cooked chick pea or hazelnut		Size of a cherry or a teaspoon					Size of a walnut or tablespoon				
Baby's Milk Needs	10 to 100 ml or 1 tablespoon to 1/3 cup per day		200 ml or almost 1 cup per day					700 to 800 ml by day or about 2 1/2 to 3 1/2 cups by day				
Frequency of Feeds	In the first month, 8 to 12 feeds per day										By about 2 months, 6 to 8 feeds per day	
Wet Diapers: Number and Wetness	At least 1 WET	At least 2 WET	At least 3 WET	At least 4 WET	At least 5 WET			At least 6 per day HEAVY WET				
Soiled Diapers: Number Colour of Stools	At least 1 to 2 per day BLACK OR DARK GREEN		At least 2 to 3 per day BROWN, GREEN OR YELLOW					About 1 to 3 large per day YELLOW			1 or more large every 1 to 7 days YELLOW	
Baby's Weight	Most babies lose about 5 to 7% of their birth weight in the first 3 to 4 days after birth. For example, a 3.2 kilograms or 7 pound baby will lose about 230 grams or half a pound.							Your baby should return to his or her birth weight by 2 or 3 weeks of age.		Your baby should gain about 100 and 250 grams a week (450 to 900 grams or 1 to 2 pounds a month) for the first 3 months.		
Growth Spurts ✳	Babies often experience a sudden burst in growth at certain times within their first few weeks. During these growth spurts your baby may want to nurse more than usual.							✳	✳			

BREAST MILK IS ALL FOOD YOUR BABY NEEDS FOR THE FIRST SIX MONTHS

The World Health Organization (WHO) and UNICEF recommend that you feed your baby *nothing but breast milk* from birth to 6 months. At 6 months, begin adding solid foods while continuing to breastfeed your baby until age two or beyond.

HOW CAN YOU TELL THAT YOUR BABY IS GETTING ENOUGH MILK?

- Your baby is sucking strongly, slowly, and steadily.
- You can see your baby swallowing.
- Your baby has a strong cry and moves actively.
- Your baby's mouth is moist.
- Your baby's eyes are bright and alert.
- Your baby comes off the breast looking relaxed and content.
- Your breasts feel softer and less full after breastfeeding.
- Your baby is growing and feels heavier.

WHERE TO FIND HELP?

Breastfeeding support is available in your community.

Ask your doctor, nurse, or midwife for help.

Your CLSC or Info-Santé CLSC can help you and refer you to communit groups or lactation counsellors.

Order a plasticized 10" x 8" format of this guid

by fax: **(418) 644-4574**

email: **communications@msss.gouv.qc.ca**

or regular mail:

**Ministère de la Santé et des Services sociaux
Direction des communications
1075, Chemin Sainte-foy, 16e étage
Québec, (Québec)
G1S 2M1**

Reprinted with the permission of:

Best start is a key program of the Ontario Prevention Clearinghouse (www.beststart.org)

Santé
et Services sociaux
Québec

Bottle-feeding

Deciding how to feed your baby is an important decision that affects your child's health and your own. You will take into account several factors before you make up your mind. You should be aware of the scientific knowledge of the unique properties of breast milk. The latest research has proven that breast milk is superior to all of the commercial infant formulas available on the market.

Breast milk gives infants all the nutrients, antibodies, hormones, immune factors and antioxidants that they need to develop. Moreover, a positive link has been observed between breast-feeding and a child's intellectual development (see "Breast milk, the ideal food for your baby," page 157). It is generally agreed that breast-fed babies do not need any other food or beverage during the first 6 months of life.

According to infant health specialists, infants who are not breast-fed are more susceptible to diarrhoea and respiratory infections, including otitis, bronchitis and pneumonia, which could increase their risk of being hospitalized. Later, such children appear to be more susceptible to obesity, diabetes, gastrointestinal disorders such as Crohn's disease or ulcerative colitis, and certain cancers, including leukemia.

Breast-feeding protects the mother's long-term health, since it reduces the risk of breast and ovarian cancer (see "Breast milk, the ideal food for your baby," page 157).

In Western nations, the quality of breast milk does not vary according to the mother's diet. Even if the mother smokes, there are unquestionable advantages to breast-feeding your baby (see "Alcohol and tobacco," "Marijuana and other drugs," and "Medication," page 196).

Breast milk is completely contamination-free, available at all times and free. It does not generate garbage such as empty containers, boxes, plastic, paper, metal, residues or polluting smoke stemming from production or transportation. Commercial infant formulas cost $700 or more during the first 9 months.

It is extremely rare for a woman to be physically incapable of breast-feeding. A mother's health problems and the consumption of prescription drugs rarely hamper breast-feeding. If you are experiencing a specific problem, consult a physician who is thoroughly familiar with breast-feeding. The problems that occasionally arise at the beginning of breast-feeding can be solved with support. It is possible, but difficult, to restore lactation once you have decided not to breast-feed or after halting breast-feeding. Lactation can also be induced in the case of adoption.

It is very important to have adequate support during the first weeks of breast-feeding. It is a satisfying experience that will continue depending on your circumstances. Regardless of how long you breast-feed, your child will benefit from it.

It is important to avoid putting pressure on yourself and to engage in this experience one day at a time. It should be noted that the introduction of a substitute for breast milk in the baby's bottle can hamper breast-feeding by affecting milk production.

When, under exceptional circumstances, a mother is unable to breast-feed because of obstetrical, neonatal or psychosocial problems, she may be disappointed or deeply saddened. It is important for these mothers to talk to an understanding individual who can help them deal with their emotions. Most important of all, the mother must console herself and, above all, avoid blaming herself, which could reduce her availability to her child.

We all know individuals who were not breast-fed and mothers who have not breast-fed their babies. Even if they are in good health, this does not invalidate the genuine short- and long-term benefits of breast-feeding. After you have read more on the question, take the time to reflect and talk about it with family, friends and other parents. This way, you can make up your mind.

What is important is to make a decision with which you are at ease and which seems the best for you and your baby.

Choice of bottles

There are several kinds of bottles on the market: glass, opaque or clear plastic, conventional or with disposable bags. They are available in 2 main sizes: 150 to 180 mL (5 to 6 oz.) and 240 to 270 mL (8 to 9 oz.). Each type of bottle has its advantages and drawbacks. Choose the type that suits you best.

Before using the bottles, wash them in hot, soapy water and rinse them thoroughly. It is not necessary to sterilize them.

There is no need to force air out of a disposable bag before giving the milk to the baby.

Choice of nipples

Latex or silicone nipples come in varied shapes, sizes and degrees of flexibility.

The size and shape of the hole affect the flow of milk. You may have to try several nipples before you find the one that is right for your baby (see "Flow from the nipple," page 219).

Some manufacturers recommend boiling the nipples for 2 to 5 minutes before using them for the first time.

Amount of milk

Whether babies are bottle-feeding or breast-feeding, **the amount of milk consumed varies a great deal from one baby to the next and from one day to the next**. Your child may be very hungry in the morning but less so in the evening. It is best to observe your infant, watch for signs of satisfaction or dissatisfaction and let her control the amount of milk she needs, depending on her appetite, as is the case with breast-feeding.

A 210- to 240-mL (7- to 8-oz.) bottle is usually sufficient to fill an infant's stomach. However, if your baby seems dissatisfied, cries and sucks her fists once she has drunk, even after burping, prepare a bit more milk. She is hungry. On the other hand, sometimes you will have to throw out the rest of the bottle.

Premature babies and infants with low birth weights usually drink small amounts but nurse more often.

Let your baby's appetite be your guide.

Generally, in a 24-hour period, your baby will drink the amounts indicated below.

AGE	NUMBER OF BOTTLES*	AMOUNT PER BOTTLE*
Up to the age of 15 days	6 to 10	45 to 115 mL (1.5 to 3.5 oz.)
15 days to 1 month	6 to 8	60 to 125 mL (2 to 4 oz.)
2 to 3 months	5 to 7	150 to 210 mL (5 to 7 oz.)
4 to 7 months	4 to 6	180 to 240 mL (6 to 8 oz.)
8 to 12 months	3 to 4	180 to 240 mL (6 to 8 oz.)
1 to 2 years	600 to 900 mL (20 to 30 oz.) per day	

*These quantities can vary from one baby to the next.

213

Milk is the best food for your child. It is more nourishing and complete than cereals. It is the only food that supplies the proteins and calcium that are absolutely essential during the first year of your baby's life. Before she starts eating solid food, your baby may drink as much as 1200 mL (40 oz.) of milk in 24 hours during a growth spurt (see "Hunger pangs," page 322).

Preparing the baby bottles

To save time, some parents prepare all of the bottles needed for a 24-hour period. Others prefer to prepare one bottle at a time. Decide what suits you best.

The dilution of infant formulas demands a great deal of attention and care to avoid mistakes, especially with powdered formula. Each manufacturer provides instructions on the can. It is important to follow the instructions exactly and measure the powder with the spoon provided, since it can vary from one brand to the next.

For the first 4 months, always dilute the formula with cooled or lukewarm water that has been boiled for one minute, according to the manufacturer's instructions (see "The type of water to use," page 231). Never use hot tap water since it can contain lead and microbes.

- First, thoroughly wash your hands.
- Assemble the items that you need.
- Wash the can with hot water before opening it with a clean can opener.

- Meticulously follow the manufacturer's instructions to dilute the milk.

- Pour the milk into the bottles and immediately put on the nipples and tops.

- Refrigerate the bottles immediately.

Keep any leftover bottles in the refrigerator for the following day.

Storing infant formula

Reconstituted milk can be stored for 1 hour at room temperature and for 24 to 48 hours in the refrigerator. Do not freeze it.

Once cans of concentrated or ready-to-serve liquid infant formula are opened, they can be kept for up to 48 hours in the refrigerator. Cover them properly.

Opened cans of powdered infant formula can be stored for up to 1 month in a dry place.

An important reminder

Milk left over after your baby's feeding must be discarded since bacteria can develop.

When to feed your baby

As the days go by, you will learn to recognize your baby's signs of hunger (see "Signs of hunger," page 172). Such signs are apparent well before your baby starts to cry. Avoid waiting for her to cry before you feed her.

If she is too warmly wrapped up, she will tend to fall asleep while feeding. If she becomes drowsy, uncover her, change her diaper and talk to her to keep her awake.

Warm up the milk

The milk must be warmed to body temperature, that is 37°C (98°F). The bottle should be neither hot nor cold to the touch.

Run hot tap water over the bag or bottle or put it in hot water for several minutes until it is warm. Gently shake the bag or bottle 10 or so times.

To check the temperature before you give the milk to your baby, squeeze out a few drops on the back of your hand or the inside of your wrist.

An important reminder

All liquid and solid foods lose nutrients or are altered in a harmful way when excessively or poorly heated.

Microwave ovens are not recommended

Microwave ovens should not be used to warm up milk since they heat it unevenly, often at overly high temperatures. Babies have been burned accidentally. Moreover, glass bottles and plastic bags risk exploding.

Giving your baby cold milk

It is not necessary from a nutritional standpoint to heat milk. However, most babies prefer warm milk, just as it comes from the breast.

Children usually start to drink refrigerated milk, water and juice at the age of 10 to 12 months. However, if your child does not like cold liquids, you can continue to warm her milk beyond that age.

An important reminder

- A disposable bag heats up more quickly than a bottle.
- Never boil a bottle or a bag of milk.
- Never pour hot milk into a disposable bag since it could burst.
- Do not warm a bottle by leaving it at room temperature.
- The warmed milk must be drunk within an hour. Discard milk not consumed within this time since bacteria multiply rapidly and could cause diarrhoea.

How to bottle-feed your baby

Take the time to get settled comfortably in a relaxing position. Slide a pillow under the arm that is supporting the baby. Make sure that your back is supported and place your feet on a stool. Tilt the bottle to keep the neck full of milk to prevent your baby from swallowing air. Vary the positions from one feeding to the next, and shift from the right side to the left side. This will help develop your baby's eyesight. It is sometimes useful to pause once or twice during feeding, especially during the first months.

It is not wise to allow your baby to have the bottle unattended in her bed. The time that you spend relaxing while feeding your baby in your arms is an investment that will quickly bring you pleasure.

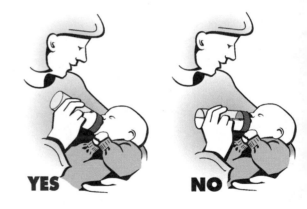

YES   **NO**

Flow from the nipple

To achieve proper suction, your baby must drink at an average pace. She must use her facial muscles. When the bottle is tipped, the milk flows very slowly. It takes just over a second for a drop to fall from the nipple.

Burping

Most babies swallow air while nursing, which causes discomfort. You must help your baby expel the air.

Burping is the first thing to try when your baby seems to be in a bad mood or squirms while drinking. Two burps are usually sufficient, the first one in the middle of drinking and the second one at the end. However, very small babies or babies who drink very quickly may need to be burped more often.

One very effective method consists of holding your baby upright on your shoulder. Gently rub or pat her back for 1 to 3 minutes.

Once your baby has burped, check to see if she is still hungry, since the air expelled may have taken the place of 30 mL (1 oz.) of milk.

If she does not burp, do not insist. Some babies do not burp. Is your baby falling asleep? Put her to bed. She may wake up crying to indicate that she needs to burp.

Washing the bottles and nipples

Rigorous hygiene is essential. It is important to carefully wash bottles, nipples and items used to prepare formula in order to avoid gastroenteritis and the development of thrush in the baby's mouth (see "Thrush in the mouth," page 395).

After a feeding, immediately rinse the bottle, nipple and bottle top in cold water. Run water through the nipple hole to remove any remaining milk.

Carefully wash all bottles, nipples and tops in hot soapy water with nipple and bottle brushes. Rinse in boiling water. Let drain and cover. You can use a dishwasher, but some manufacturers recommend against washing nipples in it.

Do not boil the nipples regularly as this could damage the rubber. Inspect them frequently. They deteriorate over time because of suction, heat, contact with milk and exposure to sunlight. Replace the nipples before they become sticky and gummy. Discard them immediately if they are pierced, torn or change texture.

If you keep the nipples and bottles clean, there is no need to sterilize them. Disposable bags are already sterilized.

An important reminder

Disposable bags are fragile and must not be reused.

Breast milk substitutes

In the case of bottle-fed babies, the Canadian Paediatric Society, Dietitians of Canada and Health Canada recommend iron-enriched commercial infant formulas up to the age of 9 to 12 months. Commercial infant formulas are better adapted to a newborn's basic needs than cow's, goat's or soy milk.

Commercial infant formulas

According to the World Health Organization (WHO) and UNICEF, it is false and biased to use the terms "humanized milk" or "baby milk" to designate commercial infant formulas since they are far removed from breast milk and human proteins. They are only substitutes for mother's milk, which is inimitable.

Purchasing infant formula

Commercial infant formulas cost roughly $20 to $35 per week. Special formulas for infants with specific problems cost more. Parents must budget for this expense for the first 9 to 12 months (see "Financial difficulties," page 149).

Formulas are sold in 3 forms:

- concentrated liquid;
- powder;
- ready to serve.

Water must be added to concentrated liquid and powdered formulas. The formulas must be precisely diluted to ensure the nutritional balance essential for your newborn's growth and to take into account the immaturity of her kidneys and digestive tract. Too much or too little water can cause digestion and health problems.

- Concentrated liquid formulas are easier to use and cost roughly as much as powdered formulas.

- Ready-to-serve products are used as is. However, they are very expensive. They are practical for occasional use on picnics or trips.

Carefully read the label in order to purchase the right product. Check the best-before date. Do not use the product if the best-before date has passed. Return cans that are dented, bulging or abnormal.

What to choose

If your child must consume milk other than breast milk before the age of 9 months, you should choose an iron-enriched cow's-milk-based regular infant formula.

Full-term babies fed infant formula exhaust the reserves of iron present at birth by around the age of 4 months. To prevent anaemia, iron-enriched formulas are recommended from birth. They are usually as well tolerated as other formulas.

Infant formula made of partially hydrolyzed proteins appears to reduce the risk of allergies among newborns in allergy-prone families.

An important reminder

Transitional formulas are not suitable for babies under the age of 6 months. They contain more calcium than conventional formulas, but less than cow's milk. They can be used to make the transition between the two types of milk but are not necessary.

Special formulas

If your baby does not appear to tolerate her milk well, consult a health professional, who may recommend a more suitable formula.

Your doctor may also prescribe a special or therapeutic infant formula. There are several kinds, including lactose-free and hypoallergenic products. These iron-enriched products are intended for babies with specific problems.

Soy-protein-based infant formulas are suitable for babies in vegan families, who do not consume dairy products.

Drug insurance plans reimburse the cost of some of these formulas when they are purchased by prescription.

Cow's milk

Cow's milk is not suited to infants. The nutrients the milk contains are perfectly adapted to a calf's needs but not to those of a human baby, at least, not before the age of 9 months.

Cow's milk contains three times too much protein and mineral salts, which overload the baby's kidneys. It provides two times less lactose than does breast milk and three times less linoleic acid, a fatty acid necessary for the development of the nervous system and the brain. It is lacking in vitamins A, B_1, B_6, C, D and E, copper, manganese and iron. It deprives the infant of important proteinic elements such as taurine, cysteine, alpha-lactalbumin and, of course, the immunological protection that breast milk provides.

Cow's milk given to infants under 9 months of age frequently causes anaemia because of the limited amount of iron that it contains and the blood loss it triggers in the intestine.

You can start to serve your baby cow's milk when she is around the age of 9 or 12 months (see "Cow's milk at 9 or 12 months?" page 272). However, do not exceed 900 mL (30 oz.) per day.

Avoid raw milk

The pasteurization of animal milk is essential. In Canada, the retail sale of unpasteurized milk is prohibited. Diseases such as poliomyelitis, typhoid, encephalitis, tuberculosis, diarrhoea, salmonellosis and brucellosis have been transmitted through raw milk. Even if the herd is in perfect health, do not give your children raw milk. The pasteurized milk sold in grocery stores is just as nutritious and is risk free.

Industrial pasteurization consists of very rapidly heating milk to very high temperatures then cooling it just as quickly. The process takes only a few seconds. Dangerous micro-organisms are destroyed without reducing the milk's nutritional value.

Home pasteurization is not recommended. It is too slow and less effective and leads to significant losses of the natural vitamins in milk (A, B_1, B_2, B_6, B_{12}, C, D and folic acid).

Goat's milk

For infants, goat's milk has the same drawbacks as cow's milk. Moreover, it has little folic acid and vitamin D.

Goat's milk enriched with folic acid and vitamin D is available in grocery stores. You can start giving it to your child from the age of 9 to 12 months, in the same way as cow's milk.

Buy whole, 3.25% pasteurized goat's milk. You can buy canned evaporated milk, which must be diluted with an equal amount of water.

Goat's milk is sometimes recommended to prevent or treat an allergy to cow's milk. Unfortunately, it often triggers intolerance. Some 80% of infants allergic to cow's milk appear to also be allergic to goat's milk.

An important reminder

Health food stores sell beverages made of soy beans, rice, almonds, and so on, which, like home-made "milks," are not suitable for infants. They are incomplete and far inferior nutritionally to breast milk or even commercial infant formulas. Babies, who grow very quickly, require a complete, balanced diet. These beverages can cause serious nutritional deficiencies that can hinder your child's development. However, they are good foods for adults.

Water

When to give water

A breast-fed baby naturally quenches his thirst at the breast, since breast milk contains more water at the beginning of each feeding. After a few minutes, breast milk becomes richer in fat and proteins. As long as your baby is breast-fed exclusively, he will not need water.

However, a baby who is fed commercial infant formula may need to quench his thirst between bottles. His crying may mean that he wants water. He will be more likely to want water when the weather is hot, he has diarrhoea or a fever. Before your baby is 4 to 6 months old, do not give him water during the hour before bottle-feeding to avoid spoiling his appetite.

When he is eating solid food, remember to give him water. Give him small amounts in a cup as soon as possible.

The type of water to use

Whether you give your baby water to drink or use water to prepare commercial infant formulas or purées, the water must always be of good quality. Some microbes that are harmless to adults can cause diarrhoea and other diseases in newborns. The water you give your baby must not have a high mineral salt content.

The following types of water are suitable:

- tap water, unless the operator of the water distribution network has advised against consuming the water;

- safe well water;

- commercially bottled non-carbonated spring water and treated non-mineralized water.

An important reminder

All of the recommended types of water, whether they are drawn from a municipal water supply, private well or spring or are bottled, must first be boiled for 1 minute when given to a baby under the age of 4 months.

How to boil the water

Put the water in a saucepan. When it comes to a full boil, time it for 1 minute. To cool it off quickly, set the saucepan in cold water.

Do not use an electric kettle as it contains deposits. Moreover, most electric kettles shut off automatically after boiling for only a few seconds, which is insufficient.

Boiled water can be kept for 2 or 3 days in the refrigerator in a sterilized, tightly closed container, or for 24 hours at room temperature.

When your baby reaches the age of 4 months, you can give him any of the types of water recommended, unboiled.

Tap water

Water from a supply system serving more than 20 people is subject to rigorous standards. As stipulated in the *Regulation respecting the quality of drinking water* (2001), frequent water samples must be taken and 16 inorganic substances and the water's bacterial content must be regularly analysed. When the water supply system serves over 5000 residents, 41 organic substances are also analysed. When standards are exceeded, the municipality and the operator of the water supply system must contact the ministère de l'Environnement du Québec and the Direction de santé publique. If the water is unfit for human consumption, the operator of the water distribution network must notify the public on the radio, in newspapers or send notices directly to the home.

Whenever you use tap water, always let it run until it is cold, to eliminate harmful build-up of lead and copper and certain microbes found in the pipes. Use cold water to prepare commercial infant formula and for drinking and cooking. Hot water may contain more lead, contaminants and microbes, to which your baby is more sensitive. Regardless of this measure, you must first boil water given to a baby under the age of 4 months.

Well water

If the water comes from a deep (artesian) well whose quality and stability are reliable, you can give it to your child. Check the chemical and bacteriological quality of water from a new well (see "Useful addresses," "ministère de l'Environnement," page 442). Special attention is called for in the case of water from a shallow well, as this type of well is more susceptible to contamination.

Well water must be free of fecal coliforms, *E. coli* or enterococci. The total coliform count is not in itself dangerous but means that the well is vulnerable to microbiological contamination.

Nitrates can enter private wells by way of fields treated with chemical fertilizers, liquid and solid manure and defective or poorly maintained septic tanks. In heavy concentrations, nitrates are especially harmful for infants under the age of 6 months. You cannot eliminate nitrates by boiling the water. In case of doubt, have your water analysed.

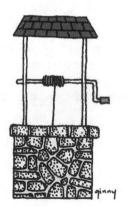

233

The maximum concentrations of the chemical substances to be monitored are as follows: nitrites and nitrates, 10 mg/L, and fluorides, 1.5 mg/L. Depending on the region where you live or the nature and proximity of human activities near the well, the water may be tested for other contaminants such as arsenic, uranium, pesticides and solvents. In case of doubt concerning the parameters to be verified in your water, contact the nearest public health branch.

Well owners must have the water analysed at their expense at least twice a year to detect *E. coli* and nitrites and nitrates, preferably after spring thaw and fall rains. The frequency of sampling may be increased if you suspect contamination.

Bottled or bulk water

Only the 2 categories indicated below are suitable for your baby. Do not use other types, especially carbonated water. Read the labels carefully.

- **Spring water**, drawn from underground springs, is suitable for human consumption and contains few minerals. Quality is monitored at the source and during bottling. It is called "natural" when it has not undergone any treatment to alter its composition.

- **Treated non-mineralized water** is tap water that has been filtered and purified to make it resemble spring water.

If you buy bulk water, remember that there is a greater risk of contamination when the containers are filled. Make sure that the source of the water is of high quality and stable. Use clean containers to store the water.

If you use a water cooler, clean it regularly according to the manufacturer's instructions.

Home water treatment equipment

In the absence of official standards and given the lack of knowledge about the safety and effectiveness of home water treatment equipment, do not give an infant under 6 months of age water treated with such equipment. Here are some of the known risks associated with water treated in this manner:

- softeners attached to the tap or the water inlet increase the sodium (salt) content of the water;

- charcoal filters (with or without silver) can increase the silver content of the water and its bacteria count;

- reverse osmosis filtering systems reduce the mineral content of the water. Some of the systems also have a carbon filter.

Moreover, all of the systems require systematic maintenance, including frequent changes of the filter or membrane.

An important reminder

- Do not give an infant mineral or mineralized water, which contains too many mineral salts.
- Do not use water from a lake, river or an uncontrolled source. Even the clearest water is not necessarily safe to drink.
- Distilled water is treated to remove most of the minerals but it is not sterile. It must be boiled.

What to do when problems arise

Has your water changed colour, smell or taste? Something is amiss. During spring thaw, such a change may be caused by calcium salt spread on roads during the winter. Farming or industrial operations can also contaminate drinking water.

- If you have problems with your tap water, contact your municipality or the private water operator.
- To check water from a private well, contact a laboratory accredited by the ministère de l'Environnement du Québec (see "Useful addresses," page 442).
- In case of doubt or to verify compliance with water quality standards, consult the ministère de l'Environnement du Québec or the Direction de santé publique.

An important reminder

If you doubt the quality of the water, do not give it to your child. Until the situation is remedied, give him water from another well or another water system whose quality is reliable or one of the recommended bottled waters.

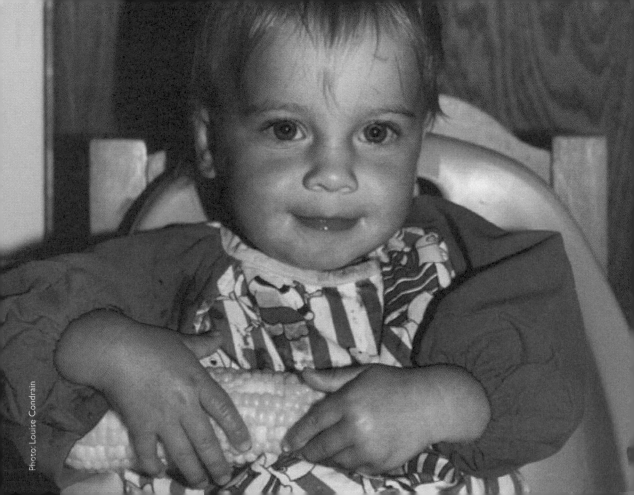

Solid Food

The introduction into your baby's diet of solid food marks the beginning of an ongoing learning process. Her first mouthfuls of solid food will serve, above all, as an initiation. Between the ages of 6 and 9 months, she will develop a taste for

foods and their different textures. Then, between the ages of 9 and 12 months, she will start to eat unaided. By the age of around 1 year, she will eat the same food as the rest of the family.

The term "solid food" applies to all foods (including fruit juice) except milk. For practical reasons, the introduction of cow's milk is also covered in this chapter.

✪ Golden rule

The advice given in this chapter applies to most babies, whether they are breast-fed or given commercial infant formula. However, it is essential to introduce solid food according to your child's pace and needs. The key is to offer her, at the appropriate time, nutritious, suitably textured foods.

At what age?

Experts agree that breast milk is sufficient to satisfy most babies' needs until the age of 6 months. They recommend introducing bottle-fed babies to solid food between the ages of 4 and 6 months.

To meet the child's nutritional needs and enable her to learn gradually to eat solid food, it is preferable to introduce such foods by the age of 6 months at the latest.

Before the age of 4 to 6 months, a baby is not usually ready to eat solid food for the reasons indicated below.

- She does not produce enough saliva.

- Her neuromuscular coordination is underdeveloped. She cannot properly set her lips to take food off a spoon or push food with her tongue in the back of her mouth.

- Up to the age of 3 months, the sucking reflex is so strong that the baby pushes away with her tongue any other food.

- She cannot sit up without support and poorly controls her neck muscles.

- She does not have the required amounts of the enzymes used to digest food.

- The newborn's still immature kidneys cannot handle an overload of too much protein.

- Her immune system is still not fully developed and there is a greater risk of her developing allergies, especially if her family is allergy-prone.

An important reminder

- There is no advantage to giving an infant solid food very early on. Such foods have less nutritional value than breast milk or commercial infant formula. Solid food consumed early on in the baby's life often replaces milk instead of complementing it.

- Do not expect your baby to sleep through the night because she eats cereal for supper. Your baby's temperament and maturity determine how long she sleeps at night (see "Sleeping through the night," page 60).

Is your baby ready for solid food?

For several days your baby's appetite has been insatiable. She is drinking a lot more than usual. You conclude that she is going through another growth spurt (see "Hunger pangs," page 322) and have increased the number of feedings or bottles. She is still hungry. Should you offer her solid food?

The answer is YES if your baby shows several of the following signs:

- she seems to be keenly interested in what you eat;

- she asks to drink more often;

- you nurse her on demand and have even increased the number of feedings for more than 3 days but she seems unsatisfied and cries even after feeding;

- she empties all of her bottles but, after feeding, she cries repeatedly and for no apparent reason other than hunger.

For many babies, this situation occurs around the age of 6 months. Solid food can be introduced fairly quickly at this stage. Some babies with good appetites demand solid food before this age and food should be introduced more gradually.

It is important to carefully observe your baby and give her solid food when she is ready for it.

Premature babies

Premature babies are introduced to solid food in the same way as full-term babies. However, you must use the baby's adjusted age, based on the anticipated date of birth (see "The age of premature babies," page 86).

◘ Golden rule

During the first year of your baby's life, milk is the basic food. Solid food complements the milk but does not replace it.

When your baby starts to eat solid food, she must continue to consume as much milk as she did before. The amount of milk will decrease subsequently. However, she must continue to breast-feed as needed or consume a minimum of 750 mL (25 oz.) of commercial infant formula.

How to introduce solid food

The order of introduction of various foods does not appear to be very important, especially if your baby starts to eat solid food at the age of 6 months. The order depends on the customs and culture of each country. What is important is to offer one new food at a time (no mixtures) and to choose nutritious foods.

In Quebec, baby cereals are usually introduced first because they are rich in iron, one of the key nutrients likely to be lacking in a milk-based diet. Next come vegetables and fruits, usually in that order. Protein-rich foods such as meat, cheese, yogurt and egg yolks are introduced last, to avoid overloading the baby's kidneys.

Texture

Initially, give your baby solid food in the form of a smooth purée. Thicken the purées as your baby gets used to eating solid food. When your baby is around 7 or 7 1/2 months old, start to serve her coarser purées. When she is 8 or 9 months old, give her soft foods cut into small pieces.

Your baby's first bites

Choose a time when your baby is in a good mood, usually at breakfast, and seat her comfortably in a quiet place. Depending on when she wakes up, this could be at the time of her first or second feeding.

First give her milk. Wait for a few minutes, burp her and warm her meal.

Feed her with a baby spoon until she indicates that she is full.

Do not give her solid food in a baby bottle.

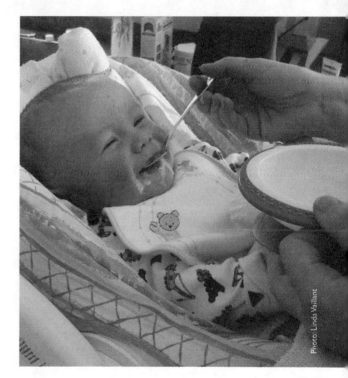

Photo: Linda Vaillant

Meal schedule

To facilitate your household routine, serve your baby her meals at more or less the same times as the rest of the family. At first, offer her cereal twice a day, for breakfast and supper. When you introduce other types of food, give your baby 3 meals a day.

New foods

Introduce only one food at a time. Wait until both you and your baby are in a good mood and relaxed. Your baby may make a face when you present a new food but she will probably accept it later on. She needs time, occasionally up to a week, to get used to new foods.

If your baby continues to refuse a new food after several days, do not insist. Reintroduce it a week or two later. It is possible that your baby simply dislikes certain flavours or textures. Like everyone else, babies have their own tastes and preferences.

Wait for 3 to 7 days before including a new food in your baby's diet. If she displays allergy symptoms, you can determine the cause (see "Food allergies," page 298).

Variable appetite

Do not be unduly concerned if your baby occasionally has no appetite, if she does not like certain foods, sometimes eats less or, to the contrary, is famished. Babies' appetites, like those of adults, vary from one day to the next.

Take into account your baby's appetite and pay close attention to the signals she sends you. A child who is hungry takes an interest in the food offered to her. Do not limit quantities if she indicates that she is still hungry. However, if she closes her mouth, scowls, pushes away the spoon, turns her head, cries or plays with her food, she is indicating that she has had enough to eat.

An important reminder

A properly balanced vegetarian diet can be suitable for an infant. However, there is a risk of nutritional deficiencies, above all in the case of a vegan diet. Consult a dietitian/nutritionist.

Honey and botulism

As a precaution, wait until your baby is 1 year old before giving her honey. Pasteurized or unpasteurized honey may contain botulism spores. When the spores develop in a young child's intestine they can cause infant botulism, a rare but often fatal disease.

Do not use honey in cooking. If you must use sugar in cooking, use plain white sugar or fructose, which tastes sweeter than white sugar, so only half or two-thirds of the suggested amount should suffice. Do not put anything sweet on a pacifier (see "How to prevent early childhood tooth decay," page 336).

How to prevent choking

Some foods can get stuck in the throat, block the respiratory tract and choke the child (see "Choking," page 387). Every year, a number of children are the victims of choking. Other smaller foods can lodge in the respiratory tract and cause an infection.

Until your baby reaches the age of 4 years, it is best to avoid peanuts, nuts, seeds, hard candies, cough drops, popcorn, chewing gum, whole grapes, raisins, sliced sausage, and raw carrots and celery.

To prevent choking:

- remove the bones from meat and fish;
- cut sausage into sticks, then into small pieces;
- quarter grapes;
- remove cores and stones from fruits.

From the age of 1 year, a baby can eat soft, raw vegetables such as mushrooms, cucumber, zucchini and tomatoes. You can serve her grated carrots. Peel and cut apples.

When your baby is 2 years old, you can give her raw vegetables cut into thin strips, peeled, whole apples, and small whole fruits, except grapes.

Always supervise your baby when she is eating. She must be seated at the table or in her high chair. Never allow your child to walk or run with food in her mouth. Do not feed her in the car. Store dangerous foods out of reach and warn older children about such foods.

Cereals: 4 to 6 months

Iron-enriched baby cereals provide your baby with additional calories, starch and some vitamins and minerals, including iron, which helps prevent anaemia.

They are an excellent choice for your baby up to the age of 2 years.

What to choose

To start, choose single-grain cereals, without added vegetables or fruit, for example, rice or barley, to limit the risk of allergies. Oat-based cereals usually contain barley and should be given later. Read the list of ingredients on the label.

Give your baby 3, 5 or even 7 days to get used to the cereal. After that time, try another kind. Once your baby is eating several simple cereals, you can give her mixed cereals. To prevent allergies, try soy-based cereals last and not before your baby is 6 months old.

Preparation

At first, make a fairly liquid paste using roughly twice as much breast milk or commercial infant formula as dry cereal. The cereal must be sufficiently liquid to spoon into your baby's mouth but thick enough that she does not suck on the mixture. Some cereals already contain powdered milk. As the directions indicate, add water only.

Quantity

Start with 3 to 5 mL ($1/2$ to 1 teaspoon) twice a day after your baby has had her milk, at breakfast and supper.

If your baby readily accepts cereal, gradually increase the amount by 5 to 15 mL (1 to 3 teaspoons) at a time until she is full. Remember that the milk she drinks already nourishes her.

By the end of the first year, the amount of dry cereal should gradually reach 125 to 175 mL ($1/2$ to $3/4$ of a cup). This amount will provide her with the recommended daily iron intake.

Refusal to eat

If your baby refuses to eat the cereal you offer, do not insist. Try again to offer it for 1 or 2 days.

If she continues to refuse the cereal, try to determine why. She may not be ready to eat solid food or she may not like the food offered or be allergic to it.

Is your baby ready for solid food? Review the relevant indicators (see page 242). If you think she is ready, try another kind of cereal.

SUGGESTED MENU AROUND THE AGE OF 4 TO 6 MONTHS

Basic food	Milk*
Breakfast	Cereal
Lunch	Cereal

* Milk: breast milk or commercial infant formula, to be given to the baby according to her needs, at least 4 times a day. The schedule of feedings will not always coincide with meals.

An important reminder

Do not put sugar on cereal as your baby prefers it plain. Too much sugar is harmful and promotes cavities. To find out if the cereal contains sugar, read the label (it may be added in the form of dextrose, maltose, sucrose, invert sugar, glucose polymer, fructose, syrup or honey).

Vegetables and fruits: 5 to 6 ¹/₂ months

You can start giving your baby vegetables 2 or 3 weeks after she starts eating cereal, and fruits 2 weeks after that.

In addition to adding a wide array of flavours to your baby's diet, vegetables and fruits provide calories, vitamins, minerals and fibre. They are necessary for good health and will help prevent constipation. Include them in your baby's diet every day.

What to choose

To start, serve your baby carrots, squash, zucchini, yellow and green beans and sweet potatoes. Serve the vegetables cooked and puréed (see "Preparation of vegetable and fruit purées," page 259).

Offer your baby one new vegetable at a time. Wait for 3 to 5 days before introducing another one. When she becomes accustomed to one vegetable, try a new one. Your baby must eat vegetables separately before eating mixtures of them.

Quantity

Start with 5 mL (1 teaspoon) of a vegetable per meal at lunch and supper. Gradually increase the amount by 5 to 15 mL (1 to 3 teaspoons) until she is full.

Nitrates and vegetables

Nitrates occur naturally in water and soil. Some vegetables, such as carrots, beets, turnips and, above all, spinach, contain heavier concentrations of nitrates. Normal quantities of nitrates found in food and water are not harmful. However, under certain conditions, they turn into nitrites, which can hinder the transport of oxygen in the blood. This transformation is more likely to occur among babies under 1 year of age, especially before the age of 6 months.

In a varied diet, vegetables do not provide enough nitrates to cause problems. However, as a precaution, wait until your baby is 9 months old before serving her beets, turnips and spinach, which have higher concentrations of nitrates. As for carrots, which babies like, you can include them among the first vegetables that you feed your baby. Until your baby is 9 months old, it is preferable to discard the cooking water and to purée the carrots with cold tap water. You should also vary the menu with the other vegetables suggested.

What to choose

At first, serve your baby apples, pears, peaches, plums, apricots and bananas. Cook and purée the fruit, except for fully ripened bananas, which can be mashed with a fork. Do not add sugar.

Offer your baby one new fruit at a time. After 3 to 5 days, when she becomes accustomed to one fruit, try a new one. Your baby must eat fruits separately before eating mixtures of them.

Quantity

Start with 3 to 5 mL ($1/2$ to 1 teaspoon) of a puréed fruit at lunch and supper, after you have given your baby cereal and vegetables. Gradually increase the amount by 5 to 15 mL (1 to 3 teaspoons) until she is full.

An important reminder

- At first, choose purées of a single vegetable or fruit.
- Avoid commercial purées or desserts containing tapioca, cornstarch, flour or sugar. These products are less nutritious than fruits.
- Do not add salt or sugar to your baby's food.

SUGGESTED MENU AROUND THE AGE OF 5 TO 7 MONTHS

Basic food	Milk*
Breakfast	Cereal
Lunch	Vegetables and fruit
Supper	Cereal, vegetables and fruit

* Milk: breast milk or commercial infant formula, to be given to the baby according to her needs, at least 4 times a day. The nursing schedules of some babies do not coincide with meal times.

Fruit juice

Juice is not essential. To quench your baby's thirst between feedings, water is preferable (see "When to give water," page 230).

Juices, like fruits, provide calories, vitamins and minerals. However, they contain virtually no fibre. You may introduce fruit juice when your baby is drinking from a cup, around the age of 6 months, preferably when she is already eating fruit.

Give her the juice in a glass or cup, never in a bottle. Do not allow her to sip the juice for long periods, even from a cup. Juice is naturally sweet and this habit increases the risk of infant cavities (see "Beware of sugar," page 340).

Fruit juice can cause diarrhoea when served too cold and in excessive quantities. Serve reasonable amounts of juice at room temperature. Juice must not replace milk and foods that are essential to your baby's growth and health.

To avoid spoiling her appetite, do not give her juice less than 1 hour before meals.

What to choose

Choose unsweetened 100% pure pasteurized fruit juices. It is not necessary to buy special products for babies. They are identical to ordinary juice and cost more.

Start with apple or grape juice, which most babies tolerate well, and wait until later to give your baby mixed juices. At first, give your baby juices extracted from only one type of fruit. If they contain pulp, strain them.

Quantity

An infant can drink between 60 and 90 mL (2 to 3 oz.) of pure juice a day. At first, dilute the juice with an equal amount of water.

An older child can drink between 125 and 180 mL (4 to 6 oz.) a day.

An important reminder

- Do not give your child too much juice. Sipping at juice can spoil the child's appetite and promotes infant cavities (see "How to prevent early childhood tooth decay," page 336).
- Avoid fruit-flavoured drinks, beverages, cocktails, punches or flavour crystals, which are not juice. They are prepared with sugar and have little nutritional value. Look for the indication "pure juice" on the label.
- Freshly squeezed juice bought from the producer and certain juices sold at refrigerated counters are not pasteurized. They can contain harmful bacteria to which young children are especially sensitive.

Meat and poultry: 6 to 7 ½ months

Roughly 2 weeks after you start feeding your baby fruit, add meat to her diet. Even if you have begun feeding her solid food early on, do not serve her meat before she is 6 months old.

Like milk, meat provides proteins. It also provides vitamins and certain minerals, especially iron and zinc. The body readily absorbs the iron it contains. During her first year of life, your baby needs a small amount of meat.

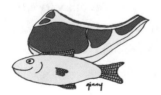

SUGGESTED MENU AROUND THE AGE OF 6 TO 7 ½ MONTHS

Basic food	Milk*
Breakfast	Cereal
Lunch	Meat, vegetables and fruit
Supper	Cereal, vegetables and fruit

* Milk: breast milk or commercial infant formula, to be given to the baby according to her needs, at least 4 times a day. The nursing schedules of some babies do not coincide with meal times.

What to choose

At first, give your baby lamb, chicken and turkey. Then try veal, beef, pork and liver (the latter can be served once a week). Serve the meat puréed until your baby is 9 months old, as it is hard to chew.

Quantity

Start with 3 to 5 mL ($^{1}/_{2}$ to 1 teaspoon) at lunch. Maintain this quantity for several days, then increase it by 5 to 15 mL (1 to 3 teaspoons) at a time, depending on your baby's tastes and appetite.

An important reminder

- Never give your baby spiced meats, smoked or other sausage, ham, salami and so on. These products contain a lot of fat, salt, spices, nitrates and other ingredients that are harmful to children. Moreover, your baby risks choking on sausage (see "How to prevent choking," page 248).

- You can give her well-cooked game meat. Make sure that the game was handled hygienically where it was shot and that the lead pellets and the flesh they have touched have been removed. However, the organs of game animals are not recommended, as they are often contaminated.

Homemade purées

Homemade purées have excellent nutritional value. They often cost less than commercial purées and are fresher, tastier and more varied than their commercial counterparts. They contain only the ingredients you choose. Of course, you will have to devote the time needed to make them, but you will quickly discover that preparing purées is easier than it seems.

Buying produce

Choose the freshest vegetables and fruits possible. Take advantage of specials. If you use frozen products, they must not contain salt, sugar, sauce or seasonings. Meat must be lean and of good quality. Avoid canned vegetables, meat and fish, which are salty. You can use canned fruit if it is canned in pure fruit juice.

Hygiene

Wash your hands and carefully wash all utensils before you make purées and each time you change from one food to another.

◘ Handy hint

Do you know other parents with a baby the same age as yours? Why not get together to cook purées and make it an enjoyable experience? Community groups organize cooking groups for this purpose. Contact your CLSC for more information.

Preparation of vegetable and fruit purées

Wash all vegetables and fruits before cooking them. Peel and remove cores, stones and seeds. Cut them into pieces.

259

Cook vegetables and fruits (except bananas) in a bit of boiling water, steam or cook them in a microwave oven until tender. Well-cooked foods are more easily digested. If they are overcooked, they lose vitamins and minerals.

Put a small amount at a time of the fruits or vegetables in a blender or food processor and purée while gradually adding enough liquid to obtain the desired texture. Use the cooking water, except in the case of carrots, to which cold tap water should be added (see "Nitrates and vegetables," page 253). It is not usually necessary to add liquid to fruits. Do not add sugar, salt, butter or other seasonings during or after cooking. Babies prefer the natural taste of foods and do not need these added ingredients.

Prepare not more than 500 g (1 lb.) of each type of vegetable and fruit at a time, which will yield 250 to 500 mL (1 to 2 cups) of purée. Avoid making overly big quantities of purées. The period during which your baby eats only purées is short and she will quickly move on to foods that are mashed or cut into small pieces.

Preparation of meat purées

Remove the skin from poultry and visible fat from meat. Cut the poultry or meat into pieces.

Cook in lots of water until tender. You can add vegetables such as onions, celery and carrots halfway through cooking in order to enhance the flavour.

Put the meat or poultry (without the vegetables) in a blender and purée while gradually adding enough cooking liquid to obtain the desired texture. Do not add salt or other seasonings during or after cooking.

Prepare not more than 250 g (¹/₂ lb.) of meat at a time, which will yield roughly 250 mL (1 cup) of purée.

Freezing

Pour the warm purée into ice cube trays, cover and cool in the refrigerator. Put the trays in the freezer for 8 to 12 hours. Once the purée is frozen, put the cubes in a plastic freezer bag. Squeeze out the air. Remember to write the type of food and the date on the bags before storing them in the freezer.

Storage

TYPE OF PURÉE	REFRIGERATOR	FREEZER
Vegetables, fruit	2 to 3 days	6 to 8 months
Meat, poultry and fish	1 to 2 days	1 to 2 months
Meat with vegetables	1 to 2 days	1 to 2 months

Note: Do not refreeze a thawed purée.

FREEZER

An important reminder

Never add salt to purées and never
use salted bouillon to make them.

Salt can contribute to the development of

hypertension and overload a baby's kidneys,

thus increasing the risk of dehydration.

Commercial purées

Commercial purées in jars or frozen are nutritious,
always ready to serve and practical. However,
they usually cost more than homemade purées.
Moreover, purées in jars sometimes contain
superfluous ingredients such as starch, sugar, flour,
tapioca, and cream. Read the list of ingredients
on the label. Choose simple foods without
unnecessary ingredients.

- **Vegetable and meat mixtures** are sometimes practical. However, the proportion of
  meat is usually small, especially in small jars
  (there is more meat in frozen preparations).
  By choosing simple purées, you can control
  the amount of meat your baby eats and serve
  the vegetables of your choice.

- **Commercial "junior" purées** are very smooth with small lumps. They do not enable a baby to learn to chew. Stop serving them as soon as your child readily accepts foods that have been mashed with a fork (see "Flavours and textures," page 266).

- **Ready-to-serve meals** contain salt. Do not give them to your child before the age of 12 months. They are of limited use, since at that age your baby can eat the same foods as the rest of the family.

Purchase and use

- Do not use chipped jars or jars with rusty lids.

- The lids must pop when opened. If they do not, avoid using the product as it is not fresh. Return the jars to the store.

- Store the jars according to expiry date. Use the oldest jars first.

- The manufacturers use colour or other codes on the labels to indicate at what age their products should be given to babies. These indications are general. Compare them with the recommendations in this chapter and check to see if they suit your baby.

- Avoid feeding your baby directly out of the jar. Put the amount of food you need in a small bowl and promptly refrigerate the remainder to avoid contamination. You can also freeze some of the food.

How to warm purées

If possible, warm only the amount of purée you need. Before you serve it to your child, check the temperature by placing a small amount on the inside of your wrist or the back of your hand. Always discard the uneaten reheated purée.

Fresh or refrigerated purée

Warm the purée in a small saucepan or a double boiler over low heat on the stove. For small amounts, put the purée in a glass bowl and set it for a few minutes in hot water. You can also use a plastic warming dish, a convenient, inexpensive way to keep food warm during the meal.

Frozen purée

Warm the necessary number of cubes for several minutes in a double boiler.

Microwave ovens

Be careful when using a microwave oven. Since the oven heats food unevenly, the purée could be cold in places but scalding in others. If you use a microwave oven, bear in mind the following precautions:

- Empty food from jars into a microwave-safe dish as the jars could burst.

- Avoid heating very small portions since they become boiling hot in a few seconds.

- Thoroughly mix the food, wait 30 seconds, then check the temperature of the food on the back of your hand or the inside of your wrist before serving it.

- Fully explain the procedure to babysitters, or suggest another way to warm your baby's food.

Flavours and textures: 7 to 9 months

Now that your baby has tasted foods from all of the food groups, learning about flavours and textures will become important at meal time.

From the age of 7 months, if she does not choke, she can eat thicker, lumpier purées made quickly in the blender or mashed with a fork.

At the age of 8 or 9 months, let her pick up small pieces of soft foods such as well-cooked vegetables, very ripe or canned fruits, and so on. Even if she has no teeth, she can chew with her gums. Your baby loves to chew. Be careful, since she risks choking on some foods (see "How to prevent choking," page 248).

Milk

During the first year, breast milk and iron-enriched commercial infant formulas are the basis of your baby's diet. After the age of 6 or 7 months, her daily milk consumption will drop gradually in favour of solid food to roughly 750 to 900 mL (25 to 30 oz.). In the case of breast-fed babies, the reduction occurs naturally.

Once you have introduced all of the food groups, breast milk or infant formula can be offered before or after solid food. What is important is to ensure that your baby receives everything she needs. Some mothers first breast- or bottle-feed the baby only partially, then give her solid foods. They pause and end the meal with the rest of the milk. Do what your baby is comfortable with.

Cereal

Continue to give your baby iron-enriched baby cereal every day. You can now offer her soy-based and mixed cereals.

Around the age of 9 months, she should eat enough cereal in the morning, that is, roughly 125 mL (1/2 cup), to satisfy her daily needs. It will no longer be necessary to serve her cereal for dinner.

Photo: Annie Fournier

Vegetables

Your baby is already eating several vegetables. Add new ones such as cauliflower, broccoli, asparagus, peas, potatoes, corn, Brussels sprouts and avocado. Make thicker and thicker purées. For variety, mix the vegetables that she has already eaten.

Around the age of 8 or 9 months, you can cut into small pieces vegetables that you have prepared for the rest of the family, provided that you have cooked them without salt. Wait until your baby is 9 months old before serving her spinach, turnips and beets (see "Nitrates and vegetables," page 253).

Fruits and juice

Your baby is already eating fruits. Add new ones such as mangoes, pineapple and melon. Mix those that she has already eaten as you see fit and according to her tastes. Gradually offer her fruits mashed with a fork, then pieces of very ripe fruit for her to pick up.

Small fruits such as strawberries, raspberries, blueberries, blackberries and gooseberries must be puréed and strained to eliminate skins and seeds. Pre-strained commercial purées are sold in jars but they also contain superfluous ingredients such as starch and sugar.

To avoid spoiling your baby's appetite, do not serve her more than 60 to 90 mL (2 to 3 oz.) of juice a day diluted with water and strained, if need be. Give her the juice in a glass or cup. Do not give her juice at bedtime (see "How to prevent early childhood tooth decay," page 336). To quench her thirst, give her water instead.

Egg yolk

Try giving your baby egg yolk 2 or 3 weeks after introducing meat to her diet. It must be fully cooked, never raw or runny. To easily separate the yolk from the egg white, prepare a hard-boiled egg.

Start with 5 mL (1 teaspoon) of cooked egg yolk mixed with a bit of milk or added to cereal or vegetables. Increase the quantity to roughly three yolks a week. Wait until she is 12 months old before serving her a whole egg since egg whites are more allergenic (see "Preventing allergies," page 301).

Legumes and tofu

To replace meat, you can start to give your child legumes or tofu. Red or orange lentils are the easiest to purée. Soft tofu can be puréed and mixed with puréed vegetables.

Fish

Fish is a wholesome food. It contains proteins and essential fatty acids. Unless fish is counter-indicated, you can offer it to your baby several weeks after introducing meat to her diet. If she already has allergies or if other family members suffer from them, do not give her fish before she is 3 years old.

What to choose

You can give your child many species of fish. Saltwater fish include haddock, halibut, pollock, cod, plaice (sole) and turbot. Sport fish include American shad, lake whitefish, brook and other trout (except lake trout), rainbow smelt and Atlantic tomcod.

Some fish species can contain pollutants. For this reason, it is preferable to limit consumption. Do not consume swordfish, shark or fresh or frozen tuna more than once a month. Avoid bass, northern pike, walleyed pike, muskellunge and lake trout (grey trout).

You can buy fresh or frozen fish. Canned fish is usually salted and should thus be avoided. However, unsalted canned tuna and salmon are available. You can use them.

Preparation

Fish is not sold puréed so you will have to prepare it yourself.

- Cook the fish in a court-bouillon, poach it in milk or cook it in the microwave oven, without adding salt.

- Carefully remove all bones.

- Break up the fish with a fork or purée it with the cooking liquid.

An important reminder

- Shellfish such as shrimp, crab and lobster pose a high risk of allergies. Avoid giving them to your baby before the age of 1 year and up to the age of 4 if she has developed allergies or your family is allergy-prone.

- Avoid raw fish since young children are more sensitive to the parasites it may contain.

SUGGESTED MENU AROUND THE AGE OF 7 TO 9 MONTHS

Basic food	Milk*
Breakfast	Cereal Fruit (depending on appetite)
Lunch	Meat Vegetables Fruit
Snack	Juice (if need be)
Supper	Cereal Vegetables 1/2 egg yolk (depending on appetite) Fruit

* Milk: breast milk or commercial infant formula, to be given to the baby according to her needs, at least 4 times a day. The nursing schedules of some babies do not coincide with meal times.

Achieving independence: 9 to 12 months

Your baby is eating with her fingers. Encourage her, as she is learning to feed herself. She is becoming more and more independent.

Give her part of her meals in small mouthfuls. Of course, she will get dirty and take longer to eat, but this phase will only last a few months.

Keep an eye on her. Let her chew dry foods such as toast, Melba toast and bread sticks. However, do not give her raw, hard foods such as carrots or celery, on which she could choke. If she needs to chew because she is teething, give her a solid teething ring (see "Teething," page 334).

At this stage, your child may eat less. Do not insist. Meal times will be pleasanter for the entire family and your child will learn to be guided by her appetite. She knows when she is full.

The importance of milk

Milk continues to be a basic part of your baby's diet. If she is breast-feeding, the best choice, she must continue to nurse according to her needs and your convenience. If she is bottle-fed, make sure that she gets enough formula to satisfy her needs, that is, roughly 750 mL (25 oz.) a day. Whenever possible, hold your baby to feed her instead of letting her fall asleep with her bottle (see "How to prevent early childhood tooth decay," page 336).

Cow's milk at 9 or 12 months?

You can start giving your baby cow's milk at the age of 9 months provided that her diet is varied. It should include vegetables, fruits and meat every

- unsweetened canned evaporated milk, enriched with vitamins C and D, which must be diluted with an equal amount of water.

Cow's milk must be introduced gradually over a period of approximately 2 weeks. First replace part of the commercial infant formula with cow's milk. Gradually increase the proportion of the new milk.

Given the high protein and mineral content of cow's milk, do not exceed 900 mL (30 oz.) a day.

Do not use 2% or skim milk

Young children need fat to ensure their growth and the development of their brains. It is preferable not to give them 2% milk before the age of 2 years. Skim milk and 1% milk are not recommended.

You can continue to give your child 3.25% whole milk right until she goes to school.

day, at least 125 mL (¹/₂ cup) of iron-enriched baby cereal and foods prepared with a bit of oil or margarine to satisfy her need for essential fatty acids. If your baby's diet does not include all of these foods, it is preferable to wait until she is 12 months old.

Choose 3.25% whole milk, that is:

- regular, vitamin D enriched homogenized milk; or

Cups and bottles

Your baby is perhaps already using a cup to drink a bit of water or diluted juice. You can now give her a bit of milk in a cup or glass.

At first, she will continue to receive most milk from the breast or bottle. This is normal. She still needs to nurse.

An important reminder

- Never give your baby sweetened condensed milk.
- Never give her unpasteurized milk (see "Avoid raw milk," page 225).

Yogurt

Toward the age of 7 or 8 months, when your baby's diet includes all of the food groups, you can offer her yogurt. At this age, a portion is equivalent to roughly 75 mL ($1/3$ cup).

Plain yogurt is preferable, to which you can add puréed fruits or fresh fruit cut into pieces. This is better for your child than sweetened commercial yogurts containing fruit.

Avoid low-fat or fat-free yogurts. If you make your own yogurt, use whole milk. Unlike commercial yogurt, homemade yogurt is rich in vitamin D since the milk from which you make it contains the vitamin.

Unripened cheese with fruit, such as Minigo and Petit Danone, is not yogurt. It contains puréed, sweetened fruit. You can give it to your baby when she is 11 or 12 months old.

Cheese

Children usually like cheese. Start with 30 to 60 mL (2 to 4 tablespoons) of cheese that you can serve your baby with a spoon, such as cottage, quark or ricotta. Next, give her grated or thinly sliced mild, white cheeses. One portion is equivalent to 15 g ($^1/_2$ oz.).

Some people maintain that cheese causes constipation. Cheese does not constipate a child who eats reasonable amounts of it and whose diet is balanced.

Meat, poultry and fish

Your baby needs a small portion of meat or a meat alternative at lunch and supper. A 15- to 30-mL (1- to 2-tablespoon) portion may suffice.

If she does not like meat, offer her poultry and fish more often. Replace meat with an egg, legumes, tofu and, occasionally, cheese. To satisfy her nutritional needs, make sure that she drinks roughly 750 mL (25 oz.) of milk a day and that she eats more than 125 mL ($^1/_2$ cup) of baby cereal.

When she is 9 months old, you can serve her finely ground meat. Later, she will be able to eat small mouthfuls of meat. Try fish and chicken, which are more tender then red meat.

Legumes and tofu

Like tofu, legumes such as chickpeas, lentils and dried beans are nutritious and economical. They can replace meat from time to time. They must be thoroughly cooked, puréed or mashed with a fork. One portion is equivalent to 30 to 60 mL (2 to 4 tablespoons).

Tofu can also replace meat. Purée soft tofu, or crumble or dice firm tofu. It can be added to vegetables to enhance its flavour. A portion is equivalent to approximately 30 g (1 oz.).

Whole eggs

When your baby is about 1 year old, she can begin to eat whole eggs. Serve them hard boiled, poached, scrambled or in an omelette. Eggs are a practical food and are easily digested.

Your baby can eat three eggs a week or even more if she is not eating a lot of meat.

Vegetables and fruits

Give your child a variety of diced, thoroughly cooked vegetables. Do not add salt. Serve them at lunch and supper. You can now introduce spinach, beets and turnips. You can also add foods cooked with tomatoes and onions to her diet.

Serve fruits cut into pieces at least twice a day, for dessert or as a snack: quartered grapes, pieces of orange, grapefruit or clementine, and shredded or lightly cooked apples. Give your baby not more than 60 to 90 mL (2 to 3 oz.) a day of fruit juice rich in vitamin C.

Varied cereal products

Once your child starts to eat with her hands, give her toast with butter or other spreads, pita or chapati, tortillas, bread sticks, unsalted crackers, and all kinds of pasta, either plain or with a bit of sauce. Be careful if you give your child rice as she could choke on it. Choose sticky, short-grain rice and mash it with a fork. Keep an eye on your child while she is eating.

Serve your child cereal products at lunch and supper. One portion is equivalent to $1/4$ to $1/2$ slice of bread and 30 to 50 mL (2 tablespoons to $1/4$ cup) of rice or pasta.

Continue to offer your child baby cereal for breakfast until she is at least 18 months old and, if possible, 2 years old. Your child needs the cereal to satisfy her iron needs. If she is less fond of them, add fruit, prepare the cereal with fruit juice instead of milk, and buy different flavours of cereal. If your child has a good appetite in the morning, give her half a slice of toast or several mouthfuls of unsweetened, ready-to-serve cereal to eat with her hands.

Baby biscuits and teething cookies are sweetened and are not necessary (see "Teething," page 334).

Snacks

Your baby may now want a snack. It must be nutritious but small. Roughly 2 hours before mealtimes, give her nourishing foods that will not spoil her appetite, such as pieces of fruit, cheese, yogurt or squares of dried bread. You can give her a bit of milk or fruit juice. If she is thirsty, you can give her water.

SUGGESTED MENU AROUND THE AGE OF 9 TO 12 MONTHS

Basic food	Milk*
Breakfast	Cereal Bread Fruit (depending on appetite)
Snack	Fruit cut into pieces (if need be)
Lunch	Ground meat, poultry or alternatives (fish, legumes, tofu, egg yolk or whole egg) Pasta, bread or crackers Vegetables cut into pieces Fruit cut into pieces
Snack	Fruit cut into pieces, juice, yogurt or cheese
Supper	Ground meat, poultry or alternatives (fish, legumes, tofu, egg yolk or whole egg) Pasta, bread or crackers Vegetables cut into pieces Fruit cut into pieces or yogurt

* Milk: breast milk or commercial infant formula, to be given to the baby according to her needs, at least 3 times a day.
  The nursing schedules of some babies do not coincide with meal times.

Photo: Pascale Turcotte

An important reminder

- Your baby does not need chocolate, ice cream, fried foods, soft drinks and candy. These foods have little nutritional value and some of them promote cavities.

- Do not give your baby coffee, tea or alcoholic beverages.

The family menu: 1 to 2 years

Your baby's menu is now highly varied and she has tried almost all of the foods eaten by the family. She is eating her 3 meals a day with you and probably needs 1 or 2 snacks. You can start to give her cooked foods with a bit of salt.

By the time your baby is 1 year old, she will have tripled her birth weight. Her rate of growth will slow somewhat and her appetite will drop off, until the age of 5. Your baby is now walking and toddling about or will soon be doing so. Everything interests her. She is eating less because her attention is elsewhere and she has less need of food.

Some parents worry about this change. If your child is healthy, happy, having fun, and growing and developing normally, do not worry.

However, if she is less active, often sick, and small for her age, see a health professional (see "Poor appetite," page 305).

Mealtime made easier

Spoons fascinate babies. Leave a spoon out for your baby to play with while you feed her with another spoon. She will gradually learn how to use it properly. Encourage her to eat at her own pace with her fingers or a spoon.

By the age of 18 months or so, your baby will be drinking properly from a cup, although she may still tip it over when she sets it down. Fill the cup only half full. At the age of 2, she will be much more skilful: she will be able to eat properly with a spoon and hold her glass with one hand.

At mealtimes, avoid loud, distracting noises from the television or radio, which may divert your baby's attention from her meal. Present food attractively, as babies adore colour. Give her small portions so that she does not get discouraged. Wait until your baby has finished the main course before serving dessert to the rest of the family, otherwise she will lose interest in her food. If this situation occurs repeatedly, it can lead to nutritional deficiencies.

However, do not force your child to eat everything on her plate. Her appetite will vary from day to day. She has her own tastes and preferences. It is important to bear this in mind.

Good habits

When possible, get your baby used to sharing the family menu. Follow the rules in *Canada's Food Guide to Healthy Eating* (see page 288). Prepare meals that include items from the 4 food groups, that is, grain products, vegetables and fruit, milk products, and meat and alternatives.

Buy simple, wholesome, nutritious, minimally processed foods. Some ingredients do not promote the health of newborns or the rest of the family. These include salt, all forms of sugar (sucrose, glucose, fructose, and so on) and products containing harmful fats such as shortening, hydrogenated oils and coconut, palm and palm-kernel oils. Read the labels.

✪ Golden rule

Breast milk is still the ideal food for children between 1 and 2 years of age. Do not hesitate to breast-feed your infant if you want to.

Dairy products

If your baby has not been fed breast milk, she should now drink cow's milk. Until the age of 2 years, give your baby 3.25% homogenized whole cow's milk. She needs fat for growth and development.

You can replace part of the milk with dairy products. A 125-g (4-oz.) portion of yogurt or 30 g (1 oz.) of firm cheese replaces 150 mL (5 oz.) of milk. To satisfy her vitamin D needs, she must drink at least 600 mL (20 oz.) a day. However, she should not exceed 900 mL (30 oz.), as she needs room for other foods.

Chocolate milk is a good substitute for children who drink little plain milk but it contains a lot of sugar. Ice cream, frozen yogurt and unripened cheese with added fruit are good desserts, although they do contain sugar.

Weaning bottle-fed babies

Unless your baby is breast-feeding, she should now drink her milk from a glass during the day. However, she may still need a bottle to satisfy her need to nurse or to ensure that she receives sufficient milk. Save the bottle for the times that your baby most desires it, for example, early in the morning and in the evening. Try to gently wean her from this habit.

Do not let your baby fall asleep or walk around with her bottle (see "How to prevent early childhood tooth decay," page 336).

Grain products

At every meal, serve your baby grain products, preferably containing whole grains, such as bread, pita, chapati, macaroni, spaghetti, pizza crust, crackers, rice, and so on. At this age, one portion is equivalent to 50 mL ($1/4$ cup) of pasta or $1/2$ slice of bread.

Continue to give her a 125- to 175-mL ($1/2$- to $3/4$-cup) serving of baby cereal at breakfast, which provides her with iron.

You can also occasionally offer your child ready-to-serve whole grain breakfast cereals containing little sugar, for breakfast or as a snack.

Vegetables

Give your child at least 2 servings of cooked or raw vegetables a day. At this age, 1 portion is equivalent to 15 to 30 mL (1 to 2 tablespoons). Potatoes are good for her. You can give her tender raw vegetables such as tomato, cucumber, mushrooms, avocado, and so on. When she is around 2 years old, you can give her firmer vegetables cut into thin strips. You can enhance vegetables by adding a bit of dip containing mayonnaise and yogurt.

Fruits

Every day, give your baby at least 2 servings of fruit. One portion is equivalent to $1/4$ to $1/2$ a fruit or 30 to 50 mL (2 tablespoons to $1/4$ cup) of pieces. Give her between 60 and 125 mL (2 to 4 oz.) of fruit juice.

Serve her ripe, peeled fruits cut into pieces, with the stones or seeds removed, such as pears, peaches, melon, bananas, mangoes, kiwi fruit or papaya; sections of oranges or clementines; strawberries or grapes cut into quarters; peeled, thinly sliced apples; and puréed dates or figs.

Meat, poultry, fish and alternatives

Some children already like meat cut into pieces but others prefer finely ground or even puréed meat. To help accustom your child to meat, serve her tender, juicy meat cut into small pieces, to which you can add a bit of sauce.

Your child will probably like poultry and fish, as most children do. Occasionally serve her liver, preferably chicken or calves' liver.

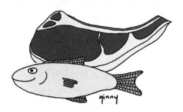

Serve sausage, smoked meat, pâté and salami only occasionally since they contain nitrates and nitrites. If you do serve them, choose the leanest, least salty, least spicy brands. Lean ham and turkey breast are good choices.

Your child must eat 2 portions of meat or alternatives a day. At this age, 1 portion is equivalent to:

- 15 to 30 mL (1 to 2 tablespoons) of meat, poultry or fish;
- one egg;
- 50 mL ($1/4$ cup) of legumes;
- 30 g (1 oz.) of tofu.

Peanut butter

Peanut butter is a practical, nutritious, inexpensive food. However, a growing number of children suffer from a serious, permanent allergy to peanuts.

If your family is allergy-prone and especially if your child has already suffered from allergies, wait until she is 4 years old before offering her peanut butter. If such is not the case, you can start to give it to your child.

To avoid the risk of choking, only give your child smooth peanut butter. Spread it thinly on warm toast.

SUGGESTED MENU AROUND THE AGE OF 1 TO 2 YEARS

Basic food	Milk*
Breakfast	Juice Cereal Bread Cheese, peanut butter or egg
Snack	Fruit
Lunch	Meat, poultry or alternative Bread, pasta or potatoes Vegetables Fruit
Snack	Fruit, yogurt, cheese, biscuits, crackers or bread and butter Juice or milk
Supper	Meat, poultry or alternative Bread, pasta or potatoes Vegetables Fruit, yogurt or light dessert

* Milk: breast milk or cow's milk, to be given to the baby according to her needs.
If she is not fed breast milk, a child of this age should consume between 600
and 900 mL (20 and 30 oz.) of milk per day, with meals or snacks.

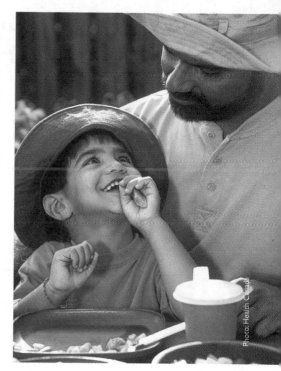

Photo: Health Canada

A sound food guide for the whole family

Canada's Food Guide to Healthy Eating is a valuable reference. It will help you plan wholesome meals for your entire family using a wide array of foods from the 4 food groups. However, it was designed for people over the age of 4. You will have to adapt it to the needs of your young children by reducing portions. Consult the table on page 290.

⭐ **Golden rule**

Your baby's and your entire family's diet should be based on the recommendations in *Canada's Food Guide to Healthy Eating*.

Grain Products
5 - 12
servings per day

 1 serving

1 slice

Cold cereal 30 g
Hot cereal 175 ml (3/4 cup)

2 servings

1 bagel, pita or bun

Pasta or rice
250 mL (1 cup)

Vegetables and Fruit
5 - 10
servings per day

1 serving

1 medium size vegetable or fruit

125 ml (1/2 cup) fresh, frozen or
canned vegetables or fruit

Salad
250 mL (1 cup)

Juice 125 ml
(1/2 cup)

Milk Products
Servings per day
Children (4 - 9 years): **2 - 3**
Youth (10 - 16 years): **3 - 4**
Adults: **2 - 4**
Pregnant and breast-feeding women: **3 - 4**

1 serving

Milk 250 ml (1 cup)

Cheese 3 in. x 1 in. x 1 in. (50 g)

Cheese 2 slices (50 g)

Yogurt 175 g (3/4 cup)

Meats and Alternatives
2 - 3
servings per day

1 serving

Meat, poultry or fish
50 - 100 g

Fish 1/3 - 2/3 can
50 - 100 g

1 - 2 eggs

Beans
125 - 250 ml

Tofu 100 g
(1/3 cup)

Peanut butter
30 ml (2 tbsp)

289

RECOMMENDED QUANTITIES OF FOODS FOR 2-YEAR-OLDS

FOOD GROUP	NUMBER OF PORTIONS	PORTION SIZE
Grain products	5	$1/2$ slice of bread 15 g of ready-to-eat cereal 75 mL ($1/3$ cup) of hot cereal $1/2$ muffin 50 mL ($1/4$ cup) of pasta or rice 4 crackers
Vegetables and fruit	5	$1/2$ of an average-sized vegetable or fruit 50 mL ($1/4$ cup) of fresh, frozen or canned vegetables or fruit 50 mL ($1/4$ cup) of juice
Milk products	500 mL (2 cups) of milk plus 1 other portion	25 g (roughly 1 oz.) of cheese 75 mL ($1/3$ cup) of yogurt
Meat and alternatives	2 to 3	25 g (roughly 1 oz.) of meat, poultry or fish 1 egg 50 g ($1/4$ cup) of tofu 50 mL ($1/4$ cup) of legumes 15 mL (1 tablespoon) of peanut butter

Food-related Problems

Colic and milk intolerance

Colic is excessive crying by a healthy baby. His face is red, his fists are clenched and his thighs are bent over his tensed stomach. Colic is usually part of the process through which a child adapts to his environment (see "Excessive crying (colic)," page 34).

However, in some instances, colic is a sign of allergies or milk intolerance.

Breast milk

Breast-fed babies also suffer from colic. There are several possible causes.

- The let-down reflex is sometimes so strong that the baby chokes while nursing and starts to cry, which causes him to swallow air. If such is the case, only give him 1 breast at each feeding. Nurse your baby before he is famished. Try to breast-feed lying down. If need be, extract a bit of milk before the feeding. If your baby chokes, briefly interrupt nursing. Burp him, if need be (see "Milk flow," page 183).

- In some instances, a newborn reacts badly to food consumed by his mother that has entered her milk. This is often true of dairy products. The risk is greater if members of your family are allergic. To check, a nursing mother should

forego milk and dairy products for roughly
I week, then reintroduce them into his diet.
If the colic diminishes significantly then returns,
it means that the baby cannot tolerate the
proteins in cow's milk. If such is the case, the
mother must consult a dietitian/nutritionist
to balance her diet. However, **if the baby's
condition does not improve, resume a
normal diet**.

- Some sensitive babies suffer more from colic
  when their mother takes an iron supplement.
  In this instance, ask your doctor for the smallest
  dose possible. A dietitian/nutritionist can draw
  up a menu that includes iron-rich foods.

- Caffeine in coffee, tea and cola beverages and
  substances in tobacco enter breast milk and
  can irritate your baby.

Intolerance to infant formula

If your baby is drinking commercial infant formula
and suffers from serious colic, it may be a sign of
intolerance. However, do not change the formula
without consulting a health professional. Frequently
changing brands is bad for the child. First consult
your doctor or another health professional.

Regurgitation

Is your baby bringing up fresh milk mixed with saliva? This means that he has drunk too much or too quickly. The valve that prevents food from flowing back toward the mouth is immature. The amounts regurgitated seem big when soaked up by a cloth but the quantity of milk is minimal, that is, roughly 5 to 15 mL (1 to 3 teaspoons). Regurgitated breast milk is odourless.

Regurgitation is a nuisance for the parents, but is usually normal for the baby. Most babies regurgitate, some more than others. If your baby is cheerful and is gaining weight, there is no cause for alarm. Your baby will probably stop regurgitating around the age of 1 year when he is more often sitting and standing up.

▶ What to do

To reduce regurgitation, check:

- how you nurse the baby or hold the bottle;
- that your baby has been properly burped;
- that you are not giving him too much milk;
- that you are not giving him the milk too quickly (see "Flow from the nipple," page 219);
- whether you handle the baby too roughly after feeding. Be gentle!

Constipation

It is not absolutely essential for a baby to have a bowel movement every 24 hours (see "Stools," page 28, and table, page 207). If he is breast-fed, he may only produce a stool every few days. Does your baby strain and turn red when having a bowel movement? If the stools look normal, do not worry. However, if they are small, hard and dry, he is constipated. Remedy the problem, as a hard stool can cause anal fissures that will encourage the child to hold on.

▶ **What to do**

Give more liquids to a newborn. Give an older child more fibre.

- Breast-fed **infants** are rarely constipated. If your baby is constipated, make sure that he is drinking enough milk (see "Is your baby getting enough milk?" page 177). Give a baby drinking commercial infant formula roughly 15 mL (1 tablespoon) of boiled water between feedings. If your baby is over 3 months of age, you can add to the water 15 mL (1 tablespoon) of warm prune, apple or pear juice. If your baby is having trouble eliminating a hard stool, insert in his rectum half or one-quarter of a glycerine suppository for babies.

- Give a **child eating solid food** water and juice, as is the case for infants. Give your baby more vegetables and puréed prunes, either alone or mixed with other fruits. If your baby is over 6 months old, add roughly 5 mL (1 teaspoon) of wheat bran to his cereal. Toward the age of 7 or 8 months, you can serve fruits and vegetables that have been mashed and, later on, cut into pieces. You can also give your child whole-wheat bread.

At the age of 9 months, give him mashed legumes. However, avoid giving your baby too much fibre and make sure that he drinks enough. Do not deprive him of rice cereal, carrots and bananas as there is no proof that they cause constipation.

If the constipation persists, your baby vomits or is growing too slowly, see your doctor. Do not give your baby a laxative without consulting a health professional.

🔲 Handy hints

- Gently move the baby's legs in a pedalling motion. Rub his tummy very gently in a clockwise motion 3 or 4 times a day.

- An overly tight diaper can hinder digestion. Undo the diaper on one side and lie your baby on his back. He will expel gas and will probably have a bowel movement.

Allergies and intolerance

A child suffers from a food allergy when his immune system reacts to a particular food that he eats. If he cannot tolerate the food, but the condition does not stem from the immune system's reaction, then he is said to suffer from intolerance.

Food allergies

The bodies of babies under the age of 6 months adapt naturally to breast milk. However, they are sensitive to foreign proteins such as those in cow's milk, which is found in all commercial infant formulas, goat's and soy milk. This sensitivity diminishes as the child grows.

Allergies in infants are usually temporary. Most of them disappear between the ages of 1 and 2 years. However, **some allergies are**

permanent and very serious. Your child is not being temperamental. A baby who is clearly allergic to a particular food must never eat the food.

How to recognize an allergic reaction

An allergic reaction can be immediate (within 2 hours of your child's consuming the allergy-causing food) or delayed, in which case the allergy is harder to diagnose. Check for the following symptoms:

- colic, repeated diarrhoea, persistent constipation, and blood in the stool (black);
- projectile vomiting;
- eczema, hives and welts;
- runny eyes and nose and stuffed nose in the absence of a cold;
- asthma, breathing problems, and swelling of the lips, tongue and throat;
- inadequate weight gain and anaemia;
- problems sleeping, irritability, and rapid changes in overall condition.

▶ What to do

If your child displays allergy symptoms, consult your doctor, who will conduct tests, if need be, to determine which food is causing the allergy.

You must eliminate the allergy-causing product. Consult a paediatric dietitian/nutritionist at the hospital or a CLSC (see "Info-Santé CLSC," page 440), who will draw up a balanced menu adapted to your child. If you are breast-feeding, stop consuming the food to which the baby is allergic. If your baby cannot tolerate regular infant formula, your drug insurance plan may reimburse the cost of a therapeutic formula.

The allergy-causing food can probably be reintroduced later. Your doctor will tell you whether your child has overcome his allergy.

Be very vigilant if your child suffers from a severe allergy. Carefully read the labels of prepared foods to ensure that they do not contain dangerous ingredients. In restaurants, ask what ingredients are used in various dishes. In case of an emergency, the child should perhaps have at hand an adrenalin injector such as EpiPen. The doctor will show you how to administer it. Ensure that the babysitter is aware of the procedure. Make sure that your child carries a card or wears a bracelet such as MedicAlert indicating his allergy.

Allergy to cow's milk

Up to 5% of babies react poorly to the proteins in cow's milk. Such proteins are found in all commercial infant formulas and may be found in breast milk when the mother consumes dairy products.

▶ What to do

If your baby is breast-fed, the mother must eliminate dairy products from her diet. If he is bottle-fed, your doctor will prescribe a therapeutic formula. Most children get over an allergy to cow's milk around the age of 1 to 2 years.

Allergy to soy-based products

An allergy to soy-based products is more complicated since soy is used in a number of commercial products, including baby cereal. As a preventive measure, introduce soy-based cereals after all other cereals in your child's diet.

Lactose intolerance

Lactose is found in breast milk and in commercial infant formulas. It is a useful sugar that promotes the development of the baby's nervous system and the absorption of calcium. Some babies are sensitive to it. They have gas and suffer from stomach aches. After a bout of gastroenteritis, the baby may develop an intolerance, usually temporary, that prolongs diarrhoea.

▶ What to do

Continue to nurse a breast-fed baby. Let him turn away from the first breast on his own before giving him the second one because the milk at the end of the feeding contains a bit less lactose. The mother can continue to drink milk. If the baby is bottle-fed, see a doctor, who may prescribe a therapeutic lactose-free infant formula to help clear up the intestinal disorder. Once the baby is better, he can continue to drink his usual milk.

Preventing allergies

Some children risk developing allergies more than others. Be especially vigilant if:

* you or your partner suffer from food or other allergies;
* your baby has a brother or sister who is allergic;
* he has already suffered from a food allergy (to milk, soy, eggs, and so on);
* he has already suffered from eczema or asthma.

To reduce and even prevent allergies, **give your baby breast milk alone for the first 6 months of his life**. It might be helpful to avoid the most allergenic foods, except in small quantities, that is, peanuts, nuts, eggs, soy, fish and seafood. Recommendations may vary depending on the family's history of allergies.

If possible, your baby should be breast-fed beyond the age of 1 year. If you wean him earlier, give him a hypoallergenic formula or a formula made from partially hydrolyzed proteins. Do not give your baby cow's, goat's or soy milk before the age of 12 months.

If your family is allergy-prone, add each food cautiously to your baby's diet and ask your doctor any questions you may have. If necessary, an allergist or dietitian/nutritionist can give specific advice.

The following table is drawn from the guide *Prévention des allergies alimentaires pour les enfants de familles atopiques*, Lise Primeau, dietitian, CHU Mère-Enfant, August 2003.

ALLERGY-RISK FOODS TO INTRODUCE AFTER:

1 year	Milk and dairy products Soy and soy-based products
18 months	Legumes (lentils, chick peas, etc.) Eggs (whites and yolks)[1]
2 years	Canned tuna and salmon
3 years	Other fish
3-5 years	Seafood, peanuts[2], nuts[2], sesame seeds, kiwi fruit.

[1] Begin by introducing them cooked in muffins, cakes, and cookies, then in pancakes and French toast, and finally alone.

[2] Whole peanuts and nuts as well as crunchy peanut butter should not be introduced before the age of 4 due to danger of choking.

Chocolate and candies can wait. A number of organizations focus on this question and can provide you with information in this respect (see "Useful addresses," page 443).

Anaemia

Anaemia is fairly common among children between the ages of 6 months and 2 years. It must be treated since it impairs the child's health and development. A baby suffering from anaemia has trouble learning, sometimes until he is of school age. An iron-rich diet is necessary to prevent anaemia. Supplements are not necessary, except for premature babies.

How to prevent anaemia

A full-term baby who is exclusively breast-fed has reserves of iron up to the age of 6 months. After that age, you must give your baby foods that contain iron. If you wean your baby before the age of 9 months, give him iron-enriched commercial infant formula.

A baby who is fed commercial infant formula exhausts his reserves of iron around the age of 4 months. As a preventive measure, give him iron-enriched formula from birth at least until he is 9 months old. Other foods he eats will provide additional iron.

A premature baby has not had sufficient time to store iron and must be given iron beginning at 2 months of age. If he is breast-fed, he should take a liquid supplement. A bottle-fed baby should be given iron-enriched formula and a supplement, if need be.

Beware of cow's milk

A baby fed cow's milk before the age of 9 months risks becoming anaemic. This milk can cause blood loss in the infant's fragile intestine, and the little iron it contains is poorly absorbed. As the child grows and consumes a variety of foods, he can drink cow's milk without the risk of developing anaemia. However, make sure that he does not consume more than 900 mL (30 oz.) a day.

Iron-rich foods

Your baby's diet must include iron-rich foods every day. The best sources are:

- iron-enriched baby cereal (keep on the menu until the baby is 2 years old);

- liver (not more than once a week);

- meat;

- tofu;

- legumes;

- egg yolks;

- green vegetables.

If he refuses baby cereal, try different varieties, add fruit to them or dilute them with fruit juice instead of milk. Does he still refuse the cereal? Buy Nutrios cereal loops or Farley's iron-enriched biscuits. You can also add baby cereal to pancakes, muffins and cookies by replacing half of the flour called for in the recipe with double the amount of dry cereal. The following recipe is an example.

Cereal-based cookie recipe

125 mL ($1/2$ cup) of butter or margarine
125 mL ($1/2$ cup) of sugar
10 mL (2 teaspoons) of vanilla
1 beaten egg
150 mL ($2/3$ cup) of white or whole-wheat flour
150 mL ($2/3$ cup) of baby cereal
6 mL ($1 1/4$ teaspoons) of baking soda
1 small pinch of salt
30 mL (2 tablespoons) of cocoa powder

Preheat the oven to 190°C (375°F). Grease 2 cookie sheets. Beat the butter and sugar until creamy. Gradually add the vanilla and the beaten egg. Fold in the flour, cereal, baking soda, salt and cocoa powder. Shape into 24 balls. Place on the cookie sheets and flatten. Bake for 10 minutes.

An important reminder

If your child is listless and has a poor appetite, is irritable, has trouble concentrating, is gaining weight too slowly or suffers from repeated infections, he may have an iron deficiency. However, these symptoms can also indicate another health problem. See your doctor.

Poor appetite

Children, like adults, sometimes lose their appetite. Loss of appetite can stem from a sore throat, teething, or the effect of medication. At other times, it is due to excitement, thrilling discoveries, fatigue or a slowdown in growth. **Children between the ages of 18 months and 2 years often experience a loss of appetite**.

Genuine diet-related problems are rare. Do not be unduly worried if your child is not eating as much as you think he should. He will not die of starvation. If his growth is normal then he is eating enough to satisfy his needs. In this instance, it is more important to make meal times enjoyable than to force your child to eat a precise amount of food.

▶ What to do

Take the time to observe what is happening in your child's life and his environment. As he grows, he wants to do more and more things on his own. Accept his awkwardness, a bit of waste and lost time without scolding him.

Give him small portions of wholesome food whose texture is suited to his age. Let him eat the way he wants, the amounts that he wants and in the order he wants. If he has not eaten anything after 20 minutes, simply remove his plate without scolding or making a fuss and let him play. Serve milk at the end of the meal.

You can give your child snacks between meals but make them small to avoid spoiling his appetite. Offer him water, milk, fruit or cheese. Avoid giving him too much juice or milk between meals.

In some cases, a vitamin and mineral supplement may be advisable. Consult your doctor or a dietitian/nutritionist to ascertain whether or not your child's nutritional needs are being met.

Is your baby too small?

If your baby does not seem to be following his growth curve, see a health professional. Your baby may not be eating enough, because of a lack of appetite, sickness, difficulty in swallowing or food intolerance. He may poorly absorb food. Perhaps your desire to feed him healthy foods means that he is getting too few calories.

Despite appearances, premature babies do not usually lag behind. Up to the age of 2 or 3 years, a premature baby's age must be adjusted in order to assess his growth (see "The age of premature babies," page 86).

▶ What to do

A doctor must examine your baby to ensure that he is not sick. Otherwise, you must adjust his diet. A hospital or CLSC dietitian/nutritionist can help you. No vitamin and mineral supplement can remedy growth retardation.

Is your baby too chubby?

There is no evidence to suggest that a plump baby will become an obese adult. Surplus fat usually disappears as the child grows.

▶ What to do

Despite social pressure, never subject a child to a weight-loss diet, regardless of his age. Do not worry if your breast-fed baby seems chubby during the first months as this is a transitional phase. To the contrary, breast-feeding reduces the risk of obesity. Continue it as long as possible. However, do teach him healthy eating habits. Encourage your child to be active and be active with him. Set a good example.

Establish regular hours for meals and snacks. Let your baby eat as much as he wants at these times but eliminate snacking (neither food nor liquids), except water. Make sure that your child eats his meals and snacks at the table, with the rest of the family. Do not rush the meal, and wait until everyone has finished the main course before serving dessert.

Before a child reaches the age of 2 years, it is not appropriate to give him fat- or calorie-reduced foods. Foods that contain a lot of fat and sugar should be avoided in his everyday diet. However, there is no harm in giving your child an occasional treat.

Take the time to observe your child. If he satisfies his need for stimulation, consolation and reward through food, pay close attention. Try to pinpoint his true need and attempt to satisfy it.

If your child develops sound eating habits and does not feel guilty about eating or his size, his weight will probably adjust as he grows taller.

Health

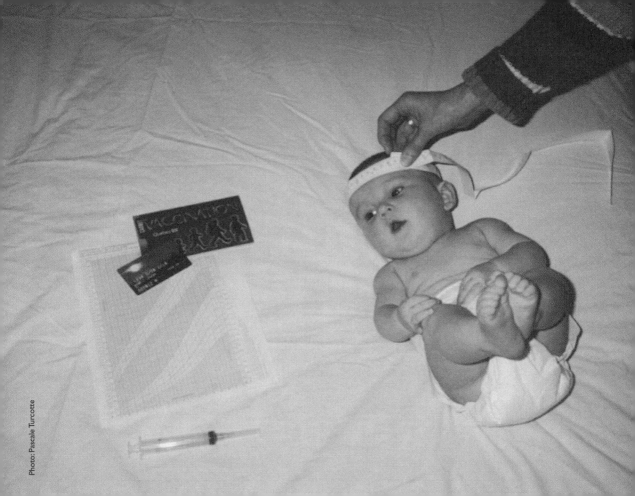

Monitoring Your Baby's Health

Monitoring your baby's health is your responsibility

To grow up strong and healthy, your baby first needs her parents. You will usually know what to do to deal with her inevitable minor problems.

However, you will sometimes have to seek the help of health professionals, who are there to care for your child and to guide and support you. This guide indicates the situations in which you should consult a health professional.

Who can help your baby?

Info-Santé CLSC

Throughout Quebec, you have access to the Info-Santé CLSC service. See page 440 for the telephone number of your Info-Santé CLSC service. This free telephone assistance is very useful. You can confidently consult a nurse 24 hours a day, 7 days a week.

You can then decide whether to see a CLSC nurse or doctor, visit a medical clinic with or without an appointment, or go to an emergency room, depending on the situation.

An important reminder

Emergency is for emergencies only

Only go to an emergency room if no medical clinic is open or your child's condition is serious. Otherwise, ask the nurse at the Info-Santé CLSC service for a list of clinics that are open.

Family doctor

Your family doctor can monitor a child who does not have major health problems. Make an appointment with your family doctor when your baby is 2 weeks old. At the first examination, the doctor will ask you questions and record information in your baby's file in order to better satisfy her needs. The doctor will examine your child again.

If possible, always go to the same clinic to ensure better follow-up. If your doctor is unavailable, his replacement will have access to your child's file, which is updated with each visit. You can also record essential information in your child's vaccination record.

CLSC nurse

CLSC nurses can help parents in various ways (see "Services offered by CLSCs," page 148). A nurse from the CLSC vaccination clinic can give your child all of the necessary vaccines according to the recommended vaccination calendar.

Midwife

Your midwife can ensure follow-up for your baby during the first 6 weeks. After that time, you must choose another professional to examine and vaccinate your child.

Paediatrician

A paediatrician can examine children with major health problems. If need be, the paediatrician who examined your infant after her birth at the hospital will make an appointment for you or refer you to a colleague. If problems arise later, your family doctor will advise you who to consult.

Dentist and dental hygienist

A dentist and a dental hygienist can help you maintain your baby's dental health, regardless of her age.

Specialists

If you think child needs specialized services, consult your doctor. Do not be embarrassed. Each child is different and has specific needs. Health professionals in hospitals and private clinics are available to help you help your child. Never hesitate to ask questions.

Some children need to see a speech therapist to learn to speak correctly. Others need to consult a special-education teacher, a dietitian/nutritionist, a physiotherapist, or an occupational therapist.

Choosing a doctor

How should you choose a doctor for your child? Talk to your family and friends and request information from health professionals. Observe the doctor's waiting room and the doctor and trust your instincts.

- Is the waiting room adapted to babies and young children?
- Is there a changing table? Are there toys to play with?
- Are children welcome?
- Do you feel at ease nursing in the waiting room?

If you do not feel at ease, you are perfectly entitled to consult another doctor.

The doctor

- Does he introduce himself to your child?
- Does he address your child by name?
- Does he smile at your child and talk to her?
- Does he place himself at eye level to examine the child?
- Does he let you hold the child as much as possible?
- Is he patient and calm even if the child does not cooperate?
- Do you feel at ease discussing your concerns with the doctor?

▣ Handy hint

Bring a book, toy or your baby's favourite blanket or stuffed animal to reassure her during the visit to the doctor's office.

How baby grows

Each baby develops at her own pace and experiences growth spurts. Premature babies grow at a slower pace. However, they catch up with full-term babies around the age of 5 years (see "The age of premature babies," page 86).

A baby gains roughly:

- 1 kg (2 lb.) per month from birth to the age of 3 months;
- 500 g (1 lb.) per month between the ages of 4 and 6 months;
- 250 g (½ lb.) per month between the ages of 7 and 12 months;
- 1.8 to 2.3 kg (4 to 5 lb.) between the ages of 1 and 2 years.

A baby's weight usually doubles between birth and around 4 or 5 months and triples by around the age of 12 months. The growth pattern of premature babies is somewhat different.

Is your baby drinking enough?

To determine whether your newborn is drinking enough **during the first 4 weeks**, pay close attention to the following points (for breast-fed babies, see the table on page 207).

Elimination – Count the number of diapers that your baby wets. After the first week, she should urinate at least 6 times in 24 hours.

Weight gain – During the first 4 weeks, an infant must gain between 20 and 30 g a day.

Growth – To determine whether your baby is growing normally, answer the questions below.

- Is she gaining weight?
- Does she seem well? Does she respond when you talk to her?
- Does she seem to have good muscle tone and a good complexion?
- Does she seem satisfied after nursing?

If you answer NO to any of these questions, your baby may not be drinking enough milk or may be absorbing it poorly. Consult a health professional (see page 314).

Growth curves

Growth curves make it possible to compare your baby's weight and height and the circumference of her head with a standard based on a group of healthy babies of the same age. A normal child's growth curve falls between the upper and lower lines and runs smoothly in one of the corridors.

The growth curve of a breast-fed baby differs from that of a bottle-fed baby. Breast-fed babies grow faster up to the age of 3 months. Conversely, bottle-fed babies grow faster between the ages of 3 and 6 months.

Photo: Louise Condrain

GROWTH CHART

Weight-for-age percentiles: Girls, birth to 36 months

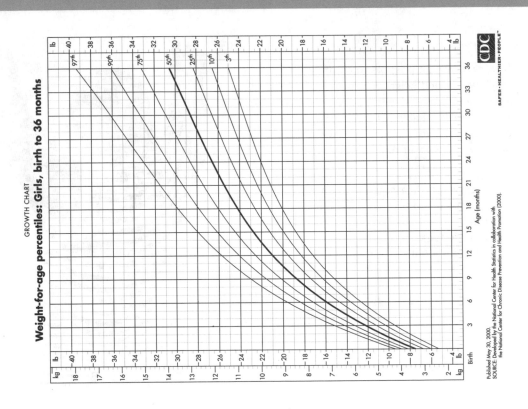

Published May 30, 2000.
SOURCE: Developed by the National Center for Health Statistics in collaboration with
the National Center for Chronic Disease Prevention and Health Promotion (2000).

SAFER · HEALTHIER · PEOPLE™

CDC

320

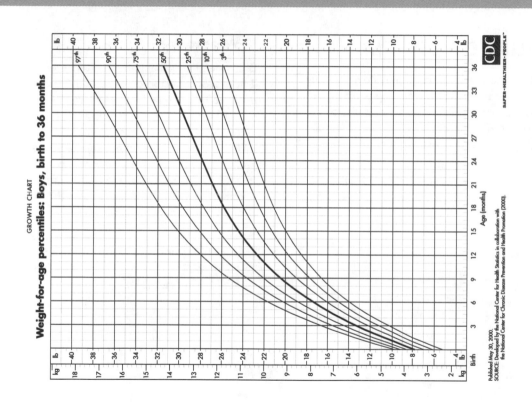

GROWTH CHART

Weight-for-age percentiles: Boys, birth to 36 months

Published May 30, 2000.
SOURCE: Developed by the National Center for Health Statistics in collaboration with
the National Center for Chronic Disease Prevention and Health Promotion (2000).

Age (months)

CDC

SAFER · HEALTHIER · PEOPLE™

Hunger pangs

During the first months of her life, your baby experiences periods of very rapid growth. Her appetite increases suddenly. She wants to nurse more often and seems dissatisfied or famished. Such growth spurts usually occur:

• between the fourth and tenth days;
• between the fourth and sixth weeks;
• around the age of 3 months.

▶ What to do

Breast-feed your baby more often, every 1 or 2 hours for a period of 24 to 48 hours. You will produce bigger quantities of more concentrated milk. Rest and eat well (see "Breast-feeding and diet," page 130). Try the handy hints to increase milk production (see "What should you do if your baby is not drinking enough?" page 178). It is preferable to persevere before introducing commercial infant formula because this situation is often temporary.

If your baby is bottle-feeding, increase the amount of infant formula you give her. Give her 15 to 30 mL ($^1/_2$ to 1 oz.) more at each feeding or feed her more often.

An important reminder

A growth spurt only lasts for a few days, after which the situation gets back to normal. Even if your baby seems famished, this is not the time to introduce solid food. An equivalent volume of solid food is less nourishing than milk. Before the age of 4 or 5 months, the introduction of new foods often causes intolerance and digestive problems.

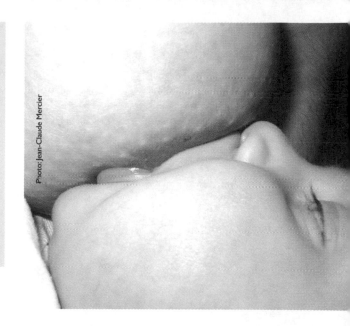

Photo: Jean-Claude Mercier

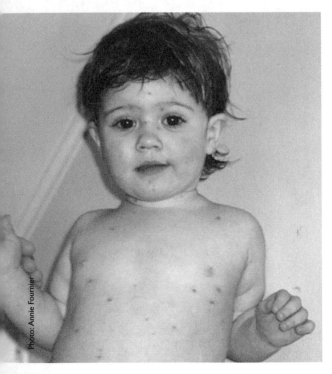

Photo: Annie Fournier

Vaccination: a protection against disease

Having your child vaccinated offers her the best protection from certain serious diseases. While these diseases have declined, they still pose a threat to your child. If vaccination were halted, the diseases would flourish.

In addition to being effective, vaccines are very safe. Of the millions of doses administered each year, very few cause serious reactions. It is better to be vaccinated than to risk catching one of the diseases the vaccination prevents.

All children should receive the recommended vaccinations, even those who are in good health and who are eating properly. Breast-feeding protects against several infections but does not prevent your child from catching the diseases prevented by vaccination.

Vaccines and the immune system

Some parents are afraid that vaccines will exhaust the child's immune system. To the contrary, vaccines stimulate the immune system. The body naturally produces antibodies against the thousands of microbes found in the air, in food, in water and on objects. Vaccines enable a child to produce her own antibodies against the disease without experiencing the harmful effects of the disease itself.

Where and when to vaccinate your baby

You can have your child vaccinated at the CLSC or by your doctor when she is 2 months old. It is important to follow the vaccination schedule. Your child must receive several doses of the vaccine to produce sufficient antibodies to fight the disease. **By having each vaccine administered as soon as your baby reaches the recommended age, you are offering her the best protection.**

RECOMMENDED VACCINATION SCHEDULE

DTap-Polio-Hib	Pneumococcus*	MMR	Meningococcal group C	Chicken pox*	Hepatitis B	d₂T₅ or DTap
This combined vaccine protects against: **d**iphteria (D) **t**etanus (T) **p**ertussis (aP) **Polio**melitis (Polio) **H**æmophilus influenzæ type **b** infections (Hib)	This vaccine protects against serious pneumococcus infections (meningitis, bacteriemia, pneumonia)	This combined vaccine protects against: **m**easles (M) **m**umps (M) **r**ubella (R)	This vaccine protects against serious meningoccal group C infections (meningitis, meningococ-cemia)	This vaccine protects against chicken pox	This vaccine protects against hepatitis B	This combined vaccine protects against: **d**iphtheria (d_2) **t**etanus (T_5) **p**ertussis (aP)

SCHEDULE (RECOMMENDED AGE AT WHICH VACCINE SHOULD BE ADMINISTERED)						
2 months 4 months 6 months 18 months Between 4 and 6 years (without the Hib)	2 months 4 months 6 months Between 12 and 18 months	12 months 18 months	12 months	12 months	Grade 4 (3 doses)	Between 14 and 16 years, followed by a booster shot every 10 years of a vaccine against diphtheria and tetanus (d_2T_5)

* The Canadian Paediatric society also recommends that you have your child vaccinated against chicken pox and serious pneumococcus infections. These vaccines are still not administered free of charge to Quebec children (June 2004). Consult your doctor or CLSC vaccination clinic.

Possible reactions to vaccines

Vaccines can cause redness, sensitivity or swelling where the injection was made. Apply a cold compress to soothe these reactions. If a small bump (nodule) appears, do not worry. It will disappear within a few weeks. When the injection is administered in the thigh, the child may also limp, although the situation is only temporary.

Between 15 and 20% of children develop a fever after being vaccinated. If this is the case with your baby, acetaminophen (see "Fever medications," page 405) will soothe her. If the fever persists for more than 48 hours or your child cries abnormally, consult your doctor. MMR (measles, mumps and rubella) vaccine can cause a fever between 5 and 12 days after the vaccination.

Serious allergic reactions are very rare. Since they occur within minutes of the vaccination, the doctor or nurse can treat them immediately. For this reason, you should wait for 15 minutes after the vaccination.

Contraindications

There are few obstacles to having your child vaccinated. If your baby has a fever that exceeds 38.5°C or 101.3°F on a rectal thermometer, postpone the appointment. Otherwise, the fever could be mistaken for a reaction to the vaccine when your child is only sick. A child with a cold who does not have a fever can be vaccinated immediately. Otitis, a runny nose or antibiotics do not justify delaying vaccination.

Children who are allergic to eggs can now be vaccinated without problem.

Premature babies

A premature baby must receive her first vaccine at the age of 2 months, regardless of her birth weight or the number of weeks of pregnancy.

Vaccination record

This important document makes it possible to keep track of the vaccinations your child receives. Bring it with you and ask the doctor or nurse to record the vaccinations administered. Your baby's growth measurements (weight and height) and other vaccination-related information can also be recorded in the vaccination record. **Do not lose it**, as it will be useful to your child throughout her life.

Vitamins and minerals

Up to 12 months

Breast-fed babies do not need supplements, except vitamin D (see page 329). Breast milk contains sufficient amounts of the other vitamins and minerals necessary for her growth.

Bottle-fed babies do not need supplements. Do not give your baby any, even if you receive free samples. Commercial infant formula already contains all of the necessary vitamins and minerals.

After the age of 12 months

If your child is eating a variety of wholesome foods, she will obtain everything she needs. Vitamin and mineral supplements do not replace food but complement it when necessary. If you must give your child supplements, choose only those that she really needs. Only give her multivitamins on the advice of a health professional.

An important reminder

If you must give your child supplements, do not overdo it. Vitamins or minerals can poison a child much faster than an adult. Read product labels to avoid an overdose. Measure quantities exactly.

Vitamin D

Normal exposure of the skin to the sun is the best source of vitamin D. Just 5 to 30 minutes a day of exposure will ensure that the body produces enough of the vitamin. However, your baby should not be exposed directly to the sun. Moreover, winter sunlight appears to be too weak to promote the production of vitamin D.

Infants absorb a small amount of vitamin D from breast milk. While opinions are divided on the matter, Health Canada recommends a supplement, especially if the baby was born during the winter. The recommended dose is 400 IU a day from birth, that is, 1 mL of vitamin D drops, placed directly in her mouth. This supplement is recommended for your baby until her diet provides her with 200 IU per day of vitamin D, which is equivalent to roughly 500 mL of cow's milk or commercial infant formula per day.

Vitamin D is found mainly in dairy products enriched with the vitamin.

If you are bottle-feeding your baby with commercial infant formula, the formula is already enriched with vitamin D and you do not need to give a supplement.

Vitamin A

Whether your baby is breast-fed or bottle-fed with commercial infant formula, **do not give her a vitamin A supplement**. Later, she will obtain enough of the vitamin from milk, fruit and yellow, orange and dark green vegetables.

Vitamin C

Whether your baby is breast-fed or bottle-fed with commercial infant formula, **do not give her any vitamin C supplement**.

Once she is given cow's milk, a varied diet rich in fruit and vegetables should satisfy her vitamin C needs. For example, a 60- to 90-mL (2- to 3-oz.) serving of juice rich in vitamin C, half an orange or 50 mL ($^1/_4$ cup) of broccoli provide the necessary amount for the day. Cow's milk contains hardly any vitamin C.

Iron

Whether your baby is breast-fed or bottle-fed with commercial iron-enriched infant formula, **no supplement is necessary**. However, she may need a supplement if she is fed another kind of milk. Similarly, premature babies must take an iron supplement. See a health professional.

Later on, a varied diet that includes iron-rich foods should suffice (see "Anaemia," page 303).

Vitamin B$_{12}$

When a nursing mother is a vegan (she does not consume any animal products) her baby may suffer from a vitamin B$_{12}$ deficiency. To prevent such a deficiency, the mother should take a supplement (see "Breast-feeding and diet," page 130).

Fluoride

Fluoride effectively prevents tooth decay. Before you give your child a fluoride supplement, consult a health professional (see "Fluoride drops or tablets," page 340).

Photo: Chantale Pelletier

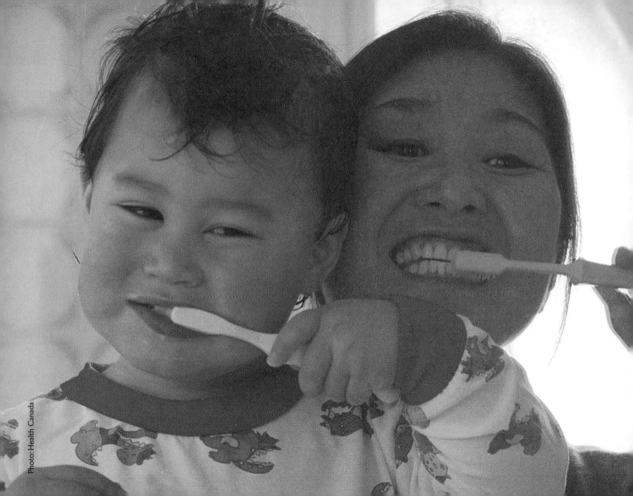

Caring for Your Baby's Mouth and Teeth

Teething

A baby's first teeth begin to form during pregnancy, which is one reason why the mother must eat well. At birth, the 20 baby or primary teeth are still forming under the gums. Your child's diet is already affecting the formation of his 32 permanent teeth.

The first baby teeth generally emerge around the age of 6 months, starting with the lower central incisors. Some babies are born with 1 or 2 teeth. Occasionally, some teeth can emerge sooner or later or are missing.

Teething may occur unnoticed or cause discomfort. A baby who is teething usually drools a lot and feels the need to bite. He may cry, refuse to eat, have a runny nose, or develop red blotches on his face or bottom. These symptoms can occur long before the tooth pierces the gum. If the discomfort is intense, consult Info-Santé since it may stem from another health problem.

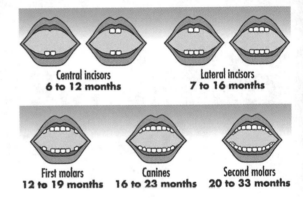

Central incisors
6 to 12 months

Lateral incisors
7 to 16 months

First molars
12 to 19 months

Canines
16 to 23 months

Second molars
20 to 33 months

Some children develop eruption cysts before the tooth emerges. This blue blister on the gum does not usually require treatment. Consult your dentist, if need be.

To soothe a baby who is teething

If necessary, give your baby a teething ring or a washcloth dipped in cold water. Refrigerate the teething ring if you wish, but do not freeze it as your baby could injure his mouth. Be sure that a recognized baby accessory manufacturer makes the teething ring. According to Health Canada, some teething toys are dangerous (see "Toys and safety," page 366).

Rub your baby's gums with a clean finger. If he is suffering a lot, give him acetaminophen (see "Fever medication," page 405).

An important reminder

- Teething syrups and gels act superficially and can reduce the baby's swallowing reflex.
- Teething biscuits do not soothe the baby and can lead to tooth decay since they contain sugar.
- As a precaution, do not give your child certain raw fruits and vegetables (see "How to prevent choking," page 248).
- Avoid teething necklaces made up of wooden balls or other small parts. According to Health Canada, they pose a choking risk.

How to prevent early childhood tooth decay

Early childhood tooth decay occurs before the age of 5 years. Your baby can suffer from tooth decay as soon as his first teeth emerge. The enamel becomes dull or changes from white to yellow or brown. Once a dental cavity starts it worsens quickly. It can be painful and hamper sleep, feeding, growth, language and self-esteem.

A young child is at greater risk of tooth decay if he often consumes sweetened beverages or foods, his teeth are not brushed properly every day, fluoride is lacking, or other members of his family are extensively affected by dental caries.

Avoid sharing

A newborn's mouth does not contain the bacteria that cause cavities. The bacteria enter the baby's mouth when he puts pacifiers, utensils and toys in his mouth or food contaminated by the saliva of a family member, babysitter or another child. The earlier on it happens, the more likely your child is to have cavities. Keep an eye on what your baby puts in his mouth.

Take care of your teeth

Take care of your teeth every day and visit your dentist regularly. Your dental hygiene will affect your child's hygiene. It will also reduce the risk of your transmitting to your baby the bacteria responsible for tooth decay.

Brush your baby's teeth twice a day

As soon as your baby's first teeth appear, brush them twice a day. An evening brushing is especially important. Use a soft-bristled child's toothbrush. Put a dab of fluoride toothpaste on the brush (see "Amount of toothpaste," page 339).

Rinse the toothbrush after each use and let it dry uncovered with the bristles pointing upward. **Make sure that it does not touch other toothbrushes to avoid spreading germs.** Your child must have his own toothbrush and not share it with anyone. Change the toothbrush as soon as the bristles are worn or bent.

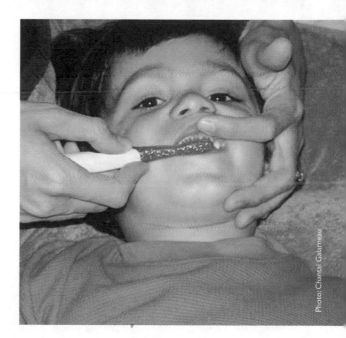

Photo: Chantal Galarneau

337

To make brushing your baby's teeth easier:

- lie your child in a safe, comfortable place; for example, on a bed, couch or carpet;

- sit behind your child in such a way that you can clearly see his mouth;

- rest his head against you;

- use the fingers of your free hand to push his lip out of the way.

Brush downward from the upper teeth and upward from the lower teeth and back and forth on the molars.

Baby's turn to brush his teeth, with supervision

Your baby becomes more independent between the ages of 13 and 18 months. He may ask to brush his teeth by himself. Encourage him while supervising his efforts. Before the age of 6 years, a child has trouble brushing his teeth correctly. **An adult must always do the final brushing.**

Children love to imitate grownups. Brushing your teeth together with your child is a good strategy.

Fluoride offers excellent protection

Fluoride is a natural substance that effectively protects against tooth decay. For this reason, it is added to toothpaste and sometimes to drinking water. It is also available in drop or tablet form.

Fluoride in water – The fluoridation of water prevents tooth decay, regardless of age. Some Quebec municipalities add fluoride to drinking water. Roughly 8% of Quebecers obtain fluoridated water. To find out if your water is fluoridated, contact city hall or your CLSC.

Amount of toothpaste – Apply a touch of fluoride toothpaste by lightly touching the opening of the tube on several bristles. The amount must not be bigger than a grain of rice. Young children tend to swallow toothpaste and too much fluoride could cause fluorosis (white spots on the teeth).

A health professional may recommend adjusting the use of fluoride toothpaste in the case of children 2 years of age or under, especially if your municipality fluoridates drinking water.

Photo: Chantal Galarneau

339

Fluoride drops or tablets – Consult your dentist, dental hygienist or doctor. He might recommend that you use fluoride drops or tablets either alone or combined with vitamins if he believes that your child has a high risk of tooth decay (see "How to prevent early childhood tooth decay," page 336).

An important reminder

- Do not give your child fluoride drops or tablets if the water he drinks is fluoridated.
- Always keep toothpaste and fluoride supplements out of the reach of children.

Beware of sugar

The more a child's teeth come into contact with sugar, the greater the risk of cavities. Unfortunately, sugar is often added to beverages, foods and medication intended for infants. Sugar also occurs naturally in fruit, juices and milk.

In baby's bottles – Do not let your child sleep or walk around with a baby's bottle or a cup containing milk, juice or any other sweetened liquid. Do not use a bottle or a cup to comfort your child. If your baby has got into these habits, dilute the contents until only water remains.

Eliminate the bottle gradually around the age of 1 year.

On pacifiers – Never dip your baby's pacifier in honey, corn syrup or any other sweetened product (see "Honey and botulism," page 247).

In snacks – Avoid giving your child sweets between meals. Unsweetened, non-sticky snacks are better for dental health. Give your child cheese, vegetables and fresh fruit. Choose unsweetened fruit juices (see "Fruit juice, What to choose," page 255). Remember that all juices contain a natural sugar. If your child drinks juice often it could promote tooth decay.

In medication – If your child takes sweetened medication, syrups or vitamins, thoroughly clean his teeth afterward or at least rinse his mouth with water.

As a reward – Avoid rewarding your child with candies, juice, fruit drinks or soft drinks.

Check your child's mouth often

Check the appearance of your child's teeth. Watch out for dull-white or brownish spots near the gum, which may indicate the beginning of a cavity (see "How to prevent early childhood tooth decay," page 336). Consult your dentist or your CLSC dental hygienist.

Visit the dentist

Your baby can first see a dentist around the age of 1 year. The Régie de l'assurance maladie du Québec pays for the dental examinations and some dental treatments of children under 10 years of age. **Cavities in baby teeth must be treated**. The dental hygienist at your CLSC can also provide information.

Photo: Health Canada

Need for sucking

All newborns have the reflex to suck. Sucking the breast is both natural and ideal for your baby. It is more demanding but more satisfying than any of the alternatives.

Not all newborns need a pacifier. Some babies are content with the breast (see "Pacifiers and bottles" in the chapter on breast-feeding, page 176).

If your child sucks his thumb or fingers, encourage him to stop this habit as soon as possible. Try a pacifier. You can better control its use.

Sucking his thumb, fingers or a pacifier can alter the position of your baby's teeth. Once your child reaches the age of 2 or 3 years, help him to gradually abandon this habit. It is important that he do so before his first permanent teeth appear. A dentist or dental hygienist can advise you.

Choice of a pacifier

If your baby needs a pacifier, choose one adapted to his age. There are several silicon or latex models.

Cleaning the pacifier

Before you give your baby a new pacifier, disinfect it as directed by the manufacturer. Every time your baby asks for the pacifier, wash it in hot, soapy water and rinse it thoroughly. Do not put the pacifier in your mouth (see "Avoid sharing," page 336). Pull on the disc to make sure that it is firmly attached to the nipple. This safety precaution is important, especially when your baby has teeth.

Regularly check the pacifier's condition. It must be very supple. If it has changed colour or shape, is sticky or cracked, discard it immediately. **Health Canada recommends replacing pacifiers after 2 months of use, regardless of their condition.**

An important reminder

- Your baby may occasionally need a pacifier for comfort. However, he must not have it in his mouth constantly. To avoid creating a habit, gently remove the pacifier when it is no longer necessary.

- The pacifier can act as a gag. Do not be overly hasty in using it to calm your baby. He is trying to communicate with you through his crying. What does he really need? Be attentive.

- Sucking his thumb, fingers or a pacifier can sometimes affect your baby's pronunciation. A child who speaks with a pacifier in his mouth is incomprehensible and does not learn to express himself correctly.

- If your baby is chewing his pacifier, give him a teething ring (see "Teething," page 334). He could break the pacifier disc while chewing on it and choke. The disc must remain outside his mouth.

- Never hang the pacifier around your baby's neck or wrist or attach it to his bed. The string could injure or strangle him.

- To attach the pacifier to clothing, use the clips designed specially for this purpose. Do not use a safety pin, which could injure your child.

- Do not dip the pacifier in honey (see "Honey and botulism," page 247) or other sweetened products, which promote tooth decay (see "How to prevent early childhood tooth decay," page 336).

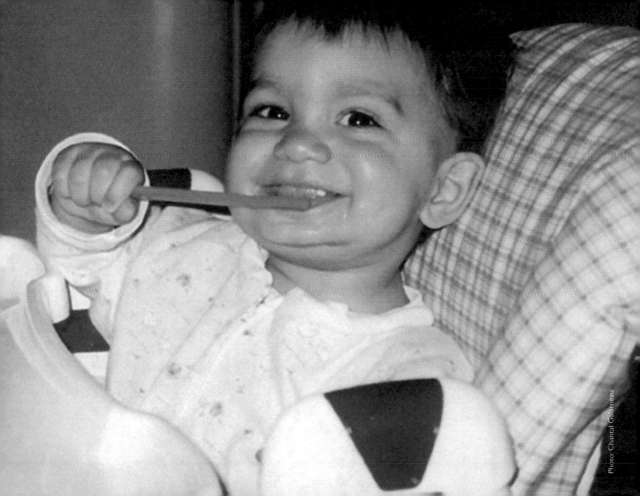

Prevention

Beware of tobacco smoke

Cigarette, cigar and pipe smoke are very harmful. Young children are especially vulnerable. The children of smokers are more susceptible than other children to asthma, earaches, bronchitis, pneumonia and upper respiratory tract infections. Exposure to tobacco smoke also increases the risk of crib death. Regardless of the number of cigarettes, there is no safe exposure to tobacco smoke.

If you smoke, smoke outside the home

Smoking in the home threatens the health of your loved ones as much as your own health. Hazardous chemicals spread through the air even if you open the windows, run a range hood fan or smoke in only one room. A very powerful ventilation system such as those found in public places takes up to 3 hours to eliminate the smoke from a single cigarette. For the sake of your child's health, do not smoke in your home or car.

Butt out

The only way to protect your child against the harmful effects of tobacco is to stop smoking. Give yourself a break. Your baby will be grateful to you, now and later on. More smokers' children than non-smokers' children take up smoking as teenagers.

A health professional can explain the various methods used to stop smoking. A number of community agencies also provide support. Contact your CLSC. To obtain information and support in kicking the habit, call the J'ARRÊTE! help line at 1 888 853-6666.

Your baby's safety

Your baby develops very quickly up to the age of 2 years. She explores her environment without realizing the dangers that lurk there. Be alert! Be doubly vigilant if your baby is active. She can escape your surveillance in the twinkling of an eye.

Falls, burns, drowning, poisoning and choking are important causes of death among children. Protect your child by creating a safe environment. **Check every room in your house from a child's eye-level view.** Block staircases. Lock drawers and the gate to the swimming pool. Cover electrical outlets with solidly installed insulating caps. Store toxic products in a safe place. An accident can happen quickly. By adapting your house to your baby, you will reduce the risk of her having an unpleasant experience.

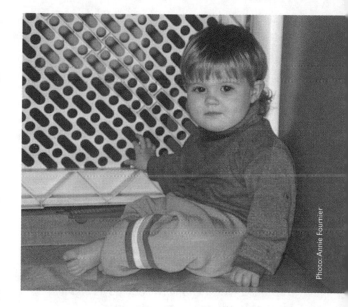

Photo: Annie Fournier

349

Your baby's room

The bedroom must be bright and well ventilated. If possible, it should have a window. Heat it to approximately 20°C (68°F). If your child perspires at night, she is too heavily covered.

Humidity should be maintained between 30% and 45%, never more. Avoid, if possible, the use of a humidifier. If you do use a humidifier, clean it and change the filters according to the manufacturer's directions. Change the water every day. Every 3 days, wash the humidifier with soapy water and disinfect it with a solution of one part bleach to 9 parts water. If condensation appears on the windows, the humidity is too high and will cause mildew. Avoid rugs that absorb humidity and trap dust. Wood and vinyl floor coverings are preferable and easier to maintain.

Children love to play in their rooms. Make sure that your baby's room is safe (see "Small objects," page 372, and "Power cords," page 374).

Blinds

The pull cords of blinds must be kept well out of the reach of children, who could strangle themselves playing with them. Attach blind and drapery pull cords throughout the house in such

Clothespin | Wind the cord around itself | Equalizing buckle | Cleat

a way that children cannot reach them. **Place your baby's bed far from the window.**

Inexpensive PVC-based mini-blinds can cause lead poisoning and neurological problems in children. Health Canada recommends getting rid of such blinds. Check the product label when buying blinds to see if they contain lead.

Your baby's bed

Baby beds manufactured prior to 1986 no longer comply with the Health Canada regulation on product safety and may not be sold. Manufacturers and retailers are well aware of the regulation. Consumers can be confident that new baby beds now comply with current standards. Avoid using beds that were given to you or beds sold in used furniture stores, at flea markets or garage sales.

Check your baby's bed regularly to ensure that it is in good condition. The sides of the bed must be raised and locked when the baby is in bed. The mattress should be firm and fit snugly on the bed, with no more than 3 cm (1 1/8 inches) between it and the frame of the bed. Movable hooks that support the bottom of the bed are prohibited. Make sure that the springs are solidly anchored. They must not move. The space between the bars should not exceed 6 cm (2 3/8 inches).

If you attach toys to the bed, the cords must not be more than 15 cm (6 inches) long. Never leave a young child unsupervised on a big bed.

You can use an antique cradle during the first month of your baby's life. Beyond that age it is dangerous to do so.

351

There are risks for your baby when she sleeps in her parents' bed, which are greater when the mother or baby have been exposed to cigarette smoke during pregnancy or after birth. Moreover, the baby should never share the bed of someone who:

- smokes;
- has consumed alcohol;
- is sick;
- has taken medication or any substance that induces sleep;
- is extremely tired.

These conditions increase the risk of crib death.

An important reminder

- You can install your baby's bed in your room.
- Always lay your baby ON HER BACK to sleep, never on her side or tummy.
- If you find it easier, breast-feed your baby in your bed. We recommend that you put your baby in her own bed to sleep.
- If you have consumed alcohol, taken medication or other substances that can make you drowsy, or if you are unusually tired, do not put your baby in your own bed, even for feeding.
- Do not sleep with your baby on a sofa or any other stuffed furniture.

- Waterbeds are dangerous for young children. A baby lying on her stomach could suffocate.
- Animals must not sleep in the same bed as the baby.
- When you are visiting or staying in a hotel, it is dangerous for a baby to sleep in an adult bed, even more so if she is surrounded by pillows, which can suffocate her. A baby can sleep safely on a floor covered with a big, thick blanket. Portable playpens can also be safe. However, do not add a mattress, cushions, pillows or anything else used as a mattress.

Bedding

The only bedding you need is a fitted sheet for the mattress and a blanket. Wash and thoroughly rinse the sheets before using them. Avoid cushions or decorative fabric for bedskirts, pillows, bolsters, quilts and stuffed animals as your baby could suffocate against these objects.

When your baby starts to move around, objects should be avoided since she could use them to climb out of bed and injure herself in a fall. Regularly check blankets for dangling threads. Do not leave blankets on your baby's bed when she is awake. She could become tangled up in them and suffocate.

Check the borders and stitching of comforters and blankets for dangling threads.

Take the following precautions if members of your family are subject to allergies.

- Destroy dust mites, which live off dead skin and thrive in warm, damp beds, by frequently washing sheets in very hot water.

- Put a zippered plastic cover on the mattress. Cover the zipper with adhesive tape.

- Do not use feather comforters and pillows.

- Avoid carpets, fabric-covered furniture, plush toys and knick-knacks that collect dust.

- Dust the baby's room with a damp cloth.

In the kitchen

Place your baby's high chair well away from kitchen counters and the table. She could push on them with her foot and tip over the high chair. Strap her into the chair to prevent her from climbing over the chair back or tray. Keep an eye on her. Some babies manage to get out of their chairs even when they are strapped in!

When your child is in a portable chair, strap her in and do not leave her unattended on the table. She could fall with the chair by kicking or trying to turn around. Put the chair on the floor instead.

When your baby begins to crawl around, keep a close eye on her. Do not put a tablecloth on the table as your baby could grab it and be injured by falling objects. Turn the handles of jugs toward the centre of the table, sideboard or counter. Do not leave kitchen utensils lying around.

Turn the handles of pots and pans away from the edge of the stove. When you are frying foods, keep your child well away to prevent her being spattered with grease or oil. Keep her away from a hot oven. She could press her hands against it.

Be careful with certain foods, on which young children can choke (see "How to prevent choking," page 248).

Staircases

Use gates to block all staircases. Solidly attach the gates to the doorframe or the walls of the hallway. If the gate is not new, check to ensure that it complies with current safety standards (see "Useful addresses," "Health Canada," page 444).

Outdoors

Be careful around swimming pools. Block access to your swimming pool by putting up a fence at least 1.2 m (48 inches) high with an automatically locking gate. Never leave the ladder down when an aboveground pool is unsupervised. Install the water filtration system more than 2 m (72$^{1}/_{2}$ inches) from the pool to prevent children from using it to climb over the fence. Put a fence around the water heater. Check the electrical ground to reduce the risk of electrocution.

Be careful, too, around shallow ponds such as water gardens. A baby can drown in 2.5 to 5 cm (1 to 2 inches) of water.

Extra vigilance is called for around lakes and rivers. Your baby can scamper away from you very quickly. Life jackets are compulsory for all passengers in boats. Properly attach your child's life jacket. If the boat capsizes, it could save your life and hers.

It is recommended that swings and other playground equipment be installed on a layer of sand or wood chips at least 30 cm (12 inches) thick. If your child falls, the consequences will not be as serious as when she falls on gravel or grass. Make sure your child is not wearing clothing with drawstrings, scarves or a bicycle helmet when she plays on such equipment.

Cover sandboxes to prevent animals from defecating in them.

When going out

Walking

Be careful when you carry your baby in a front or back infant carrier. A fall could injure you and your baby. During the winter, make sure that your baby is properly dressed, is not cold and can move her legs. Immobilizing the legs could lead to serious frostbite.

Baby strollers and carriages

There are several types of baby strollers and carriages. The choice is up to you. Convertible models, which serve as a carriage, bed and stroller, are practical year round.

One excellent choice is the stroller with an adjustable back. Your baby can be taken for a stroll or have a nap in it, under supervision, with the safety belt securely fastened.

The folding umbrella-stroller is practical but is so light that it sometimes tips forward. Make sure the child is strapped in. Make sure, too, that her fingers are out of the way when you press the folding mechanism.

Avoid overloading the stroller in order to prevent it from tipping over. Do not use it to carry packages or clothing. Be vigilant. Regularly check that screws and bolts are tight and that the brakes are working properly. Use them.

An important reminder

- Never leave a child unsupervised in her stroller or carriage.
- Never take a stroller on an escalator.

Cycling

You can carry your baby in a bicycle baby seat when she is at least 1 year old. Choose a bicycle seat with a headrest and a leg-guard. Your child must be sitting up straight with her shoulders and head supported. Remember the safety helmets: yours and your child's. Make sure that the seat is properly installed and that the straps are correctly adjusted. Refer to the manufacturer's instructions to determine the maximum recommended weight of the child. Some models are not compatible with certain bicycles.

Never leave your child in the bicycle seat if you are not on the bicycle, which could fall over. Ride slowly. It will take longer to stop when you brake. If you are not used to carrying a child on the bicycle, practise by riding the bike with a sack of potatoes that weighs as much as your child in the bicycle seat. You may prefer to buy a bicycle trailer, which has more space and can be used to transport 2 children. Properly attach the seatbelt and install a pennant to ensure visibility.

Choose cycling paths well away from roads, which are much safer. Be careful at intersections.

Traveling by car

Always use a car safety seat (see following section). If you have to nurse your baby, stop and hold her in your arms. Never leave a baby under the age of 6 months drinking from a bottle unsupervised.

Parents are advised not to buy a used car safety seat from someone they do not know. It is essential to be thoroughly familiar with the seat, which must:

- be in good condition and not be missing any parts;

- bear the manufacturer's and Transport Canada's compliance seal;

- have an instruction booklet;

- not have been involved in an accident;

- not have been subject to a manufacturer's recall (call CAA-Québec to check);

- have been manufactured **less than 10 years ago** according to Transport Canada and **not more than 6 to 8 years ago according to certain manufacturers** (contact the manufacturer for details).

Car safety seats

By law, in any moving vehicle your child must use a car safety seat adapted to her weight and height until she measures 63 cm (25 inches) or more when seated (measured from the seat to the top of the head).

The safety seat must be used from the day you leave the hospital. If you wish to rent a car safety seat before you leave the hospital, check with your CLSC.

There are 3 types of seats: infant seats, child seats and booster seats. Change the seat as your child grows. **Read carefully the manufacturer's instructions before using the seat.**

Since September 2002, all vehicles manufactured in Canada have been equipped with a **Universal Anchorage System (UAS)** (Isofix or LATCH) and all car safety seats manufactured in Canada are equipped with a belt that is attached to the vehicle's UAS, which facilitates installation.

See pages 17 to 19 for infant seats.

Child seats

As is true of infant seats, child seats properly support the child's body.

Put the child seat on the back seat of the car. The seat should face forward only if the child is able to hold herself erect (around the age of 1 year). Before then and if the seat design allows for it, the child will be safer facing backwards. Attach the seat to the vehicle using the seatbelt or the Universal Anchorage System. If the seat does not have a belt for the UAS, you can attach it separately.

When the child seat is installed facing forward, attach the restraint strap to the vehicle's anchoring point to prevent the top of the seat from tilting. The vehicle manufacturer locates the anchor bolt there. To obtain additional information on the installation of car safety seats, consult the vehicle owner's manual or contact CAA-Québec.

Put the harness in the seat slots that are higher than the child's shoulders. Make sure that the harness is taut and that the chest clip that links it is raised to the level of the child's armpits (under the arm and in the middle of the chest).

Do not leave more than 1 finger's width between the harness and the child's collarbone.

Booster seats

Booster seats are usually for children weighing more than 18 kg (40 lb.). **Carefully read the manufacturer's instructions**.

This restraint system helps to properly place the shoulder belt in the middle of the shoulder (on the collarbone) and the lap belt on the hips (and not on the stomach). Put the booster seat on the back seat of the vehicle.

It is recommended that a booster seat be used on a bench seat if the car seatback is low. The child's head must be properly supported. If the vehicle has rear seat shoulder belts, do not place the shoulder belt under the child's arm or behind her back.

Before you stop using the booster seat, make sure that the seatbelt is properly positioned on your child's shoulder and hips. The booster seat must be used for as long as is necessary.

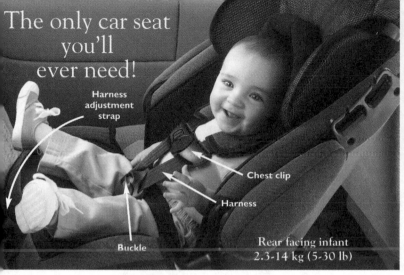

The only car seat you'll ever need!

Harness adjustment strap

Chest clip

Harness

Buckle

Rear facing infant
2.3-14 kg (5-30 lb)

Forward-facing toddler
10-18 kg (22-40 lb.)

Belt-positioning booster
18-36 kg (40-80 lb.)

Alpha Omega® Elite

is the only 3-in-1 car seat designed to grow with your child from 2.3-36 kg (5-80 lb.). It starts as a rear-facing seat for infants, later faces forward for toddlers, and eventually becomes a belt-positioning booster for older kids.

This advanced car seat features a no-rethread 5-point harness that simply and conveniently adjusts from the front of the seat to accommodate your growing child. Kids ride in complete comfort with three-position recline, and adjustable headrest and padded pivoting armrests.

Designed to grow with your child, the Alpha Omega® Elite is the only car seat you'll ever need!

OSCO
JUVENILE

Bearing in mind the weight limit recommended by manufacturers, some children are safer sitting on a booster seat even if they measure over 63 cm (25 inches) when seated.

When your child is big enough to ride in a car without a booster seat, put her in the back seat and make sure that she does up her seatbelt.

Flying

If you travel by plane with your child, you can seat her in her car safety seat if it meets the CMVSS 213, 213.1 or 213.2 standard.

Taxis

In the absence of a car safety seat, the child must wear a seatbelt unless she is too small to hold herself erect.

An important reminder

- Children under 12 years of age should be seated and belted in the back seat since it is the safest area.
- **Never install a car safety seat in the front if your vehicle is equipped with an airbag on the passenger side.** If the airbag inflates, it could seriously injure or kill your child.
- If your vehicle's seatbelts lock only upon impact, the belt that anchors the car safety seat must be equipped with a safety clip (see the manufacturer's instructions).

Baby accessories

Portable chairs

Portable chairs or infant carriers are used as chairs in the home. **It is dangerous to use an infant carrier as a car safety seat.** Until your baby is 2 months old, leave the infant carrier in the almost recumbent position. She must be comfortable without being able to turn her body. Do not set the infant carrier on a bed or other soft surface. **Never leave the child alone on a table** or elsewhere.

High chairs

High chairs must have a wide, stable base. The tray must be easy to clean. Block the tray to prevent the child from falling or slipping underneath it. As soon as a baby sits properly, she will like her chair, from which she can observe her little empire. **Make sure that she is properly strapped in.** Never leave her alone. Move the high chair away from walls, furniture, appliances and blinds.

Security gates

Accordion-style expandable security gates with large diamond- or V-shaped openings are prohibited. A baby could catch her head in the gate. Choose the appropriate model of gate, bearing in mind its use. Various models are available, including expandable, rigid, pressure, wooden, plastic and metal gates. Make sure that the gate is solidly anchored to the frame.

Playpens

Wooden – The bars must be 6 cm ($2^3/_8$ inches) apart. Raise all 4 sides of the playpen. A child could fall into the space between the mattress and the bars and suffocate. Remove from the playpen any toys on which the child could climb.

Mesh – The netting must be like mosquito netting so that nothing can catch in the holes. To ensure that the playpen remains stationary, it should not have more than 2 wheels.

A playpen may be useful for a young child while her little brother or sister is being breast-fed. The older child will be safe in the playpen, near you. When you are free to supervise her, she will enjoy getting out of the playpen to move around, crawl and explore.

An important reminder

- Do not attach pacifiers or toys with string to the playpen bars.
- Never leave your baby in a playpen with one side lowered.
- Make sure that the playpen's locking mechanism is fully engaged.
- Do not leave your baby unsupervised in a playpen.

Front or back infant carrier

The front infant carrier is very practical and infants usually appreciate it. It enables parents to move about while maintaining warm physical contact with their baby (see "Excessive crying (colic)," page 34). The back infant carrier is suitable for babies 6 months or over. In both instances, the baby snuggles against her father or mother. Choose the model that is comfortable for you and your baby. Make sure that she is warm enough when you use the carrier outdoors in cold weather (see "Baby's firt outings," page 141).

Photo: Monique Bordeleau

Baby swing

A swing takes up a lot of space and is not an essential baby item. However, a baby will find it amusing for short periods. Until your baby reaches the age of 6 months, lie her in the swing. Keep an eye on her, especially if other children push the swing.

Other accessories

Some accessories are popular, but serve no useful purpose.

Hammock – A cloth hammock can be hung over the child's bed, using 8 adjustable straps attached to the bars. It can be dangerous and does not offer the advantages of a firm, stable mattress. It is an unnecessary expense.

Walker – Walkers have been prohibited in Canada since April 2004 because they cause numerous accidents and injuries. All too often, babies using a walker fall down stairs.

Stationary activity centre – A stationary activity centre is like a walker without wheels. Never leave a child in it unsupervised. It is unnecessary since your baby needs to play on her tummy to develop strength in her arms and learn to crawl.

Jolly Jumper exerciser – We do not recommend this exerciser for the same reasons as the stationary activity centre.

Toys and safety

Toys are stimulating and contribute to a child's development. Choose attractive toys that are appropriate to her age and needs.

She will appreciate the presence of her parents or an older brother or sister to help her discover her toys and learn how to use them. She will then be able to repeat what she has learned and play more independently.

Toys must:

- be washable;
- be non-toxic (read the label);
- be unbreakable;
- be non-flammable;
- be big enough that the child cannot swallow them or put them in her mouth;
- comply with federal government safety standards (see "Useful addresses," "Health Canada," page 444).

Avoid soft vinyl (PVC) toys and rattles. They contain softening agents, some of which are toxic. A child can absorb these substances while chewing on the toy.

Before you buy

- Read product labels to determine the recommended age.

- Check that the toy is easy to handle.

- Make sure that it does not have any sharp edges or pointed tips.

- Make sure that the eyes and nose of teddy bears are properly sewn on. Big toys must not have parts that are likely to break off.

- Beware of small objects and parts. A child could put them in her nose or mouth and suffocate. A gauge is available to help parents identify toys that are dangerous (see "Useful addresses," "Health Canada," page 444). In the meantime, use a roll of toilet paper as a guide. If the object goes through the tube, keep it out of your child's reach.

- Any rattle that slides vertically through a 50-mm x 35-mm (2-inch x 1½-inch) oval opening is too small and is dangerous.

- Musical toys are fine. They stimulate the baby's hearing and eyesight. However, check the gears and make sure that small parts cannot break off.

- Be careful with noisy toys. They can damage the child's hearing and irritate you. Try them out before buying them.

- Consult the list of the best toys prepared by the Office de la protection du consommateur (see "Useful addresses," page 442). However, remember that a toy recommended for a 3-year-old child can be dangerous for a baby under the age of 1 year.

After you buy

- Read the manufacturer's instructions.

- Discard plastic, cellophane and polystyrene (Styrofoam) packaging materials.

- Be careful with spent batteries, since leaking batteries can be corrosive. Do not allow the liquid to touch your baby's skin or enter her mouth.

- Remove battery-operated toys when your child is sleeping.

- Check her toys regularly and discard broken ones.

- Discard deflated balloons. A child can choke on them if she puts them in her mouth. Only an adult should inflate balloons.

- Always keep an eye on a playing child.

Putting toys away

Get your child into the habit of putting her toys away in a basket, a lidless box or on a low shelf. When she is older, she can put her toys in a vented toy box. If the box has a lid, make sure that it is fastened in such a way that it cannot fall on the child's head or fingers.

An important reminder

- Toy guns that children buy or make are fairly popular. It is advisable to supervise children when they play with the toys, especially to avoid injury. The compulsory rule is that while playing, they must not "really" hurt anyone. The "pretend" facet of these games gives children the satisfaction of expressing their emotions and teaches them the important distinction between make-believe and reality.

- You can buy second-hand toys, furniture and other items for your baby, but be vigilant. Regulations governing these products have been tightened in recent years to ensure your child's safety. Before you buy a used product, contact Health Canada for information at 1 800 561-3350.

Be careful

In the sun

The skin is the body's largest organ. It must be protected against dehydration and exposure to blazing sunlight. While sunlight is essential for good health (see "Vitamin D," page 329), babies must not be exposed directly to the sun without proper protection, such as PABA-free sunscreen, a hat and a parasol. Babies have very thin skin that burns easily in the sun.

Before 6 months – Put your baby in the shade. Applying sunscreen to her delicate skin could cause an allergic reaction.

After 6 months – When your baby plays outdoors, make sure she wears a hat and dress her in clothing with tightly woven fibres that cover her arms and legs. Apply sunscreen to her bare skin 30 minutes before she is exposed to the sun. Repeat the application every 2 hours and after swimming. Up to 85% of ultraviolet rays penetrate clouds. Always apply sunscreen, even when it is cloudy. There are several good brands. Choose one with a sun protection factor (SPF) of at least 15. Your pharmacist can advise you.

An important reminder

- Never send a child out to play without adequate protection.
- Avoid exposure to the sun between 10 a.m. and 2 p.m.
- PABA-based sunscreens can cause allergic reactions. Baby oil does not protect your child from the sun and increases the risk of sunburn. Do not use these products.
- Never send a child to a tanning salon.
- If your child is taking medication, consult your doctor or pharmacist. Her skin may become more sensitive to the sun or certain sunscreens may cause irritation, rashes and swelling.

Eyes and the sun

Beware of all sources of radiance, whether the sun's direct rays or rays reflected off sand, water and snow. There are several ways to limit the level of harmful rays that reach the eyes:

- the natural closing of the pupil;

- wearing a wide-brimmed hat or cap, whether or not the child is exposed directly or indirectly to the sun;

- wearing protective glasses, which must block UV rays (UV 400), be of good quality, and have a scratch-proof surface.

Practical advice concerning the sun

- To protect your child from the sun, never seat her facing it. Position her (under 1 year of age) in the shade or in indirect sunlight.

- A child should never look directly at the sun, whether or not there is an eclipse.

- Do not let a child play with magnifying glasses or mirrors that could reflect the sun's rays.

- Consult an optometrist or an ophthalmologist if your child cannot tolerate even indirect sunlight or if her eyes water when she is outdoors.

An important reminder

Most sunglasses purchased from superstores are moulded shells that cause distortions for some wearers and discomfort such as headaches and, ultimately, impaired vision. **Remember that it is better to wear nothing than to wear glasses that provide inadequate protection.**

Small objects

Do not leave any of the following items lying around: buttons, thimbles, needles, marbles, matches, peanuts, safety pins, coins, jewelery, cigarette butts, pieces of paper, paper clips, beads and popcorn. Babies put everything in their mouths. They can get a serious shock by sticking an object into an unprotected wall outlet.

Avoid jewelery for babies, such as gold neck chains and rings.

After a party, quickly pick up deflated balloons, which could choke your child. Avoid tacking posters to walls as the thumbtacks will eventually fall on the floor.

Never leave razor blades, scissors, knives or plastic bags lying around. A plastic bag could suffocate your child. Tie used plastic bags in knots and discard them in a garbage can out of children's reach.

Dogs

Children are small and their size and behaviour makes them especially vulnerable to dog bites. It is usually the family dog or a dog that is known to the family that is responsible for the biting. A child is incapable of recognizing signs of aggressiveness.

A child must never be left alone with a dog, even if the animal knows the child and is seemingly inoffensive. A dog that is gentle with your child may act aggressively with other children.

Dogs do not instinctively love children. What should you do? Prepare your dog psychologically for the baby's arrival. Before your baby's birth, gradually reduce the time you spend with your dog. Push the baby carriage or rock a doll to get your dog used to your future routine. Play baby sounds for him. As soon as the baby is born, let him sniff the newborn's clothing. Speak kindly to your dog when your baby is present and ignore the animal when your baby is sleeping. He will associate the child with a source of pleasure for him.

An important reminder

- Do not allow your dog to climb on chairs or take food off the table.
- Do not take lightly any sign of aggressiveness. If your dog bares his teeth, growls or pretends to bite, consult your veterinarian or an obedience specialist.
- When visiting, be doubly vigilant if your hosts' dog is not used to your child.

Falls

Never leave your baby unattended on the table when you are changing her diaper, even for a few seconds. If she moves a lot, change her on the floor.

Do not leave footstools or low furniture near windows. A child who is crawling could climb onto them. Also make sure that no furniture or objects can fall on your child's head.

Never leave a baby's portable chair on the table, choose the floor instead.

Power cords

Remove power cords such as the cords of floor lamps running over rugs or under furniture. Do not let your baby chew on them. Unplug cords that are within her reach. Childproof socket covers should be placed solidly over wall outlets.

The power cords of electrical appliances such as irons and electric kettles should never be left dangling. When you are ironing, make sure your baby is in a safe place such as her playpen. Always keep her in your sight.

Hot water

Hot tap water can give children second- or even third-degree burns. If the water temperature is 60°C (140°F), one second of exposure can cause such burns. Children love to play with taps, so be especially vigilant.

The temperature of your water should not exceed 49°C (120°F). In households with electric water heaters, temperature control devices can be installed on the bathtub and bathroom sink taps. If you have a gas- or oil-fired water heater, set the thermostat to 49°C. An electric water heater must be set at 60°C to prevent the development of the bacteria that cause legionellosis, a severe type of pneumonia.

When you prepare a bath, run the hot and cold water simultaneously. Always check the water temperature before you put your child in the tub. Do not allow an infant to be washed by an older sister or brother.

Fires and burns

Install a smoke detector on each floor of the house and replace the batteries once a year. If need be, consult your municipal fire department. Keep a fire extinguisher on hand. Do not leave matches lying around and if you own a cigarette lighter, make sure it is has a safety lock. If you use candles for lighting, put them on a metal candleholder and keep the wicks short. Be careful of hot wax.

Children's clothing must be flame-resistant. Loose-fitting sleepwear can more easily catch fire. Choose polyester or nylon garments, which do not burn as easily as cotton.

Children have thinner skin than adults do. They are at greater risk of being burned by soup, coffee and other hot liquids. Avoid consuming such liquids when you are carrying your baby. Beware of steam and hot electrical appliances.

Hazardous products:
medication, household cleaners and other products

Each year, several thousand children between the ages of 1 and 5 are poisoned in Quebec. They have swallowed a toxic product, their eyes or skin have been exposed to such a product or they have inhaled fumes from it. These products are found everywhere: in the home, in schools and in parks.

A number of common products are toxic for children, for example: vitamins and cold medicines, cleaning products, fuel, plants, mushrooms and pesticides, nail polish remover, hair remover lotion, and hair dye. These products are found in kitchen cupboards, in the bathroom, in the bedroom, in the garage and even in your purse.

To prevent poisoning

- Keep toxic products out of the sight and reach of children.

- Store the products in cupboards or drawers with safety latches or in inaccessible places.

- Never leave medicine on the changing table or near the baby's bed.

- Keep handy the telephone number of the Centre Anti-poison du Québec: 1 800 463-5060.

Other simple measures can help reduce the risk of poisoning among children.

- When you purchase medicine and dangerous products, choose containers with safety caps, although such caps are not 100% effective.

- Store the products in their original containers.

- Avoid transferring dangerous products to food containers, for example, putting gasoline in a soft drink can.

- Keep ashtrays and alcoholic beverages out of reach.

- To avoid overdoses, carefully read the instructions on medication before giving it to your child or consult your pharmacist.

- Keep diaper bags and handbags out of your child's reach.

- When you are visiting other people, make a quick inspection to ensure your child's safety.

The Centre Anti-poison du Québec (see "Useful addresses," page 440) has published several brochures on preventing poisoning. To obtain additional information, consult its Web site (www.cchvdr.qc.ca/SoinsServices/).

Plants

The leaves and fruits of many indoor and outdoor plants are toxic and can cause skin irritation, swelling, difficulty in swallowing, dryness of the mouth, diarrhoea, vomiting and hallucinations. **As soon as your baby starts to crawl or walk, keep such plants out of her reach, give them away or discard them.**

You can obtain a list of toxic plants from the Centre Anti-poison du Québec (see "Useful addresses," page 440).

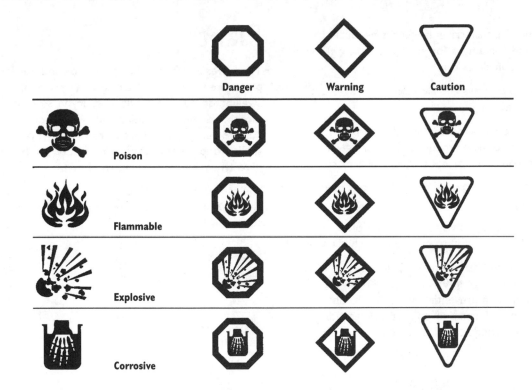

	Danger	Warning	Caution
Poison			
Flammable			
Explosive			
Corrosive			

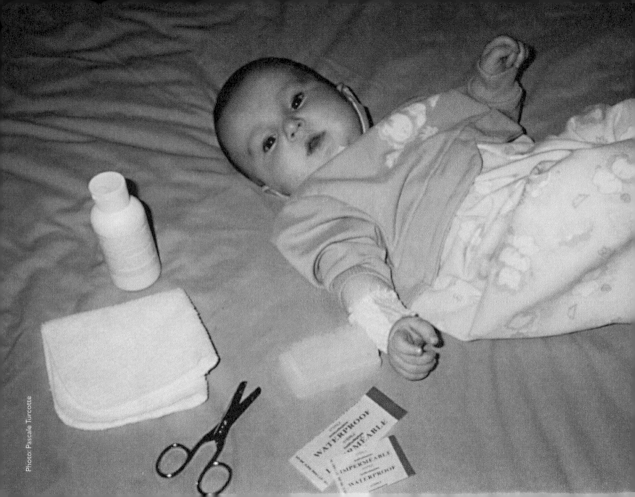

First Aid

An ounce of prevention is worth a pound of cure. However, should your child be involved in an accident, the following basic first aid tips will be useful.

Above all, stay calm.

Cuts

Deep, profusely bleeding cuts – Do not waste time cleaning the wound. Cover the wound with a clean bandage and press on it to stop the bleeding. Consult a doctor.

Small cuts or scratches – Rinse the wound with running water, then wash it with soap and water. Carefully remove dirt and stones, if need be. Put an adhesive bandage on a small wound. On a larger wound, use a pressure bandage.

You can call Info-Santé CLSC to find out whether it is necessary to consult a doctor for an examination or stitches.

Bites

If an animal or another child has bitten your child, wash the wound with running water and soap, or in a basin filled with soapy water, for 5 to 10 minutes. Rinse thoroughly and cover the wound with a dry bandage. Consult a doctor or call Info-Santé CLSC.

Nosebleeds

Babies rarely have nosebleeds, which are frequent in children. Bleeding often occurs after a cold (when the nose is irritated) or when your baby puts his finger or an object in his nostril. This is usually harmless.

First, reassure your child. Seat him with his head tilted slightly forward. Make sure he is breathing through his mouth, then use your thumb and index finger to pinch his nostrils just below the bony portion. Maintain constant pressure for at least 10 minutes, until a clot forms. After a few hours, your child can gently blow his nose.

Here are some preventive measures to follow after a nosebleed.

- Do not give your child aspirin (ASA), antihistamines (cough syrups, Benadryl, Claritin, Reactine, Aerius, and so on) and anti-inflammatory drugs such as Advil or Motrin, which alter blood coagulation.

  N.B.: Acetaminophen (Tempra, Tylenol, Abenol) does not increase the risk of nosebleeds and can be used without problem.

- Maintain the humidity in the child's room at between 30 and 45%. Use a cold-air humidifier, if need be.

Falls and blows

Your child has fallen or received a blow to the head. Is he conscious? Crying? Screaming? Howling? Although he is not bleeding, does he already have a big bump? You can apply a washcloth rinsed in cold water. Monitor your child's condition for the next few hours. Consult a doctor if the child is less than 1 year old since his condition is harder to assess, if your child displays unusual behaviour, or if he is:

- drowsy;
- vomiting (especially repeatedly);
- having trouble moving his arm or leg;
- having convulsions;
- is bruised behind the ear or under the eyes.

If your child momentarily loses consciousness, go to an emergency room.

What if his spine is fractured? This would be ill-advised.

Mouth and teeth injuries

Your child bites his tongue or lip

Gently wipe off the blood with a clean, dry cloth. To stop the bleeding, apply direct pressure on the wound. A washcloth rinsed in very cold water will prevent swelling. If the wound seems deep or continues to bleed profusely, see a health professional to find out whether stitches are necessary.

Dislodged tooth (baby tooth)

Do not put the tooth back. Put it in cold milk and avoid touching the root (the portion located in the gums). Immediately see a dentist.

Broken or shifted tooth

See a dentist as soon as possible.

A blow on a tooth

If your child falls or is struck on a tooth, the tooth may become greyish several months after the accident. Consult your dentist.

Burns

Scalding from hot liquid

If a hot liquid has touched a part of your child's body covered by clothing, do not remove it. As quickly as possible, immerse the wound or hold it under cold running water for at least 10 minutes. If the burn is hard to get at, place a clean cloth soaked in cold water over it. **Do not rub the burn.** Remove only clothing that is not stuck to the skin.

Go to an emergency room if the clothing is stuck to the skin or the burn is extensive.

An important reminder

Never put baby oil, vinegar, butter, toothpaste or oily ointment on burns as they only aggravate the situation.

Fire

Extinguish the fire before it gets out of hand. If your child's clothing is on fire, lie him down and extinguish the flames by quickly wrapping his body (except his head) in a blanket. Do not remove his clothing. Immerse the burn or hold it under cold running water for 10 minutes. If the burn is hard to get at, place a clean cloth soaked in cold water over it.

Do not rub the burn. Then, remove clothing that is not stuck to the skin.

Go immediately to an emergency room.

Electrical shock

If your child receives a shock from an electrical wire or a wall outlet not protected by a socket cover, turn off the current before moving the child away from the outlet. If the child is unconscious, call 911. If he has stopped breathing, quickly begin cardiopulmonary resuscitation (CPR). Electricity can cause serious internal burns, even when no burns are apparent on the skin. Always take the child to an emergency room, as examinations are necessary.

Foreign objects in the nose

Even though you watch your baby attentively, a small child can put all sorts of foreign bodies in his nose, for example, buttons, rocks, dried peas and peanuts.

If your child is under 18 months old, do not attempt to dislodge the foreign body as you will only push it further in. If the child is over 18 months old, you can try to remove the foreign body if it is visible, if you can grasp it and if you can keep the child's head completely still.

If you cannot remove the foreign body, take your child to an emergency room.

Sand in the eye

To remove sand from your child's eye, rinse gently with lukewarm water. If you see a small stone in the inner corner of the eye, you can try to remove it with the corner of a moistened paper tissue. Do not insist. Prevent your child from rubbing his eye and soothe him by applying a towel rinsed in cold water. Consult a doctor, if need be.

Insect bites

To protect children under the age of 2 years from insect bites, put mosquito netting on the stroller. Dress your child in clothing that covers his arms and legs. Avoid outings at sunup and sundown, when mosquitoes are most active.

Insect repellents must be used cautiously. Citronella, lavender and eucalyptus-based products are not recommended for children under the age of 2 years. Products containing DEET are not recommended for babies under the age of 6 months but soy-oil- and DEET-based products can be used on children between the ages of 6 months and 2 years when the risk of complications from insect bites is high, for example, allergies and the risk of transmitting diseases when travelling abroad. Choose DEET at a concentration of less than 10%. Apply a small amount only once a day and only to the parts of the body that are uncovered. Do not put the product on the child's face and hands.

Wash an insect bite with water and soap and apply a cold compress to relieve itching and reduce swelling. If swelling extends to other parts of the body or the child has trouble breathing, he may be having an acute allergic reaction. Immediately consult a doctor.

Choking

Your baby puts an object such as a candy, seed or piece of grape in his mouth and starts choking. He coughs, squirms and cries. Let him try to get rid of the object himself. **Do not intervene as long as he can cough forcefully.**

If he is unable to cough and is breathing with difficulty, call 911.

▶ **What to do**

A child 1 year old or under – If the child is crying weakly, is making a high-pitched sound when breathing or is turning blue, quickly lie him on his stomach on your forearm, supported by your thigh. Your baby's head should be lower than his trunk, with his face downward (see drawing). With the palm of your hand, deliver 5 quick blows to the baby's back between his shoulder blades, letting the palm slide toward the head.

If this does not work, place your baby on his back with his head lower than his body. Put 2 fingers on his sternum (between the breasts), keep the fingers straight and press quickly and release

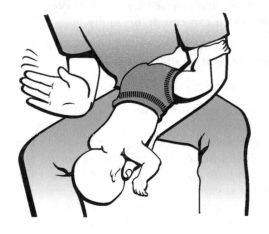

5 times without shifting the fingers. Make sure that you do not touch the tip of the sternum.

Continue administering 5 quick blows to the baby's back, then pressing the sternum 5 times in succession until the foreign object is expelled or your baby starts to breathe or cough.

When the baby has expelled the foreign body, hold him on your knees. Calm him and reassure him. Give him something to drink only if he is breathing properly. See a doctor, who will ensure that the choking and your manoeuvres do not lead to complications.

If the foregoing procedure does not work and the baby becomes unconscious, while you are waiting for the ambulance, lie your baby on his back, put one hand on his forehead to slightly tilt his head back and raise his chin with 2 fingers. Look in his mouth. If you can see the foreign object and think you can remove it easily, gently do so. If the child is not breathing, cover his nose and mouth with your mouth and blow twice. Then, with one hand on his forehead, put 2 fingers between his breasts and push toward the floor on his chest 5 times. Check whether you can see the foreign object and repeat the manoeuvres until the ambulance arrives or your baby breathes.

A child 1 year old or over – You can attempt the Heimlich manoeuvre. Stand behind your child and place your arms around his waist. Make a fist with 1 hand, cover it with the other hand and place it on the abdomen, just above the navel. Then exert a quick inward and upward pressure.

Repeat until the foreign body is expelled.

Poisoning

Among children under the age of 4 years, poisoning is the second biggest cause of hospitalization after falls. It often occurs in the home. Medication such as vitamins, antibiotics, products such as Tempra or Advil and household products such as cleaners, fuel, cosmetics and plants, are the leading causes of poisoning among young children.

▶ **What to do**

If you suspect that your child has been poisoned, **follow the procedure indicated below**.

- If the child has stopped breathing or is unconscious, call 911.

- If the child has swallowed the dangerous product, immediately call the Centre Anti-poison du Québec at 1 800 463-5060.

- If the toxic substance has come into contact with his eyes or skin, rinse abundantly with clear water, then call the Centre Anti-poison du Québec at 1 800 463-5060.

The Centre Anti-poison du Québec is an emergency service that operates 24 hours a day. Staff will tell you what to do depending on the child's condition, the product in question and how the poisoning occurred (through ingestion or contact with the skin or eyes).

An important reminder

- **Do not induce vomiting.**
- **Do not administer any treatment such as activated carbon or a vomiting agent unless a nurse from the Centre Anti-poison du Québec or a health professional recommends it.**
- Milk is not an antidote.
- Do not attempt to neutralize the product.
- Keep the product that caused the poisoning to show it to the doctor, if need be.

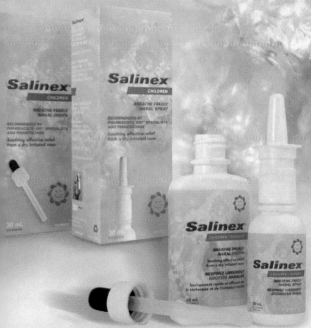

Salinex®

BREATHE FREELY!

RECOMMENDED BY PHARMACISTS, ENT SPECIALISTS AND PEDIATRICIANS

A saline solution for soothing effective relief from a dry irritated nose.

SAFE for CHILDREN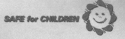

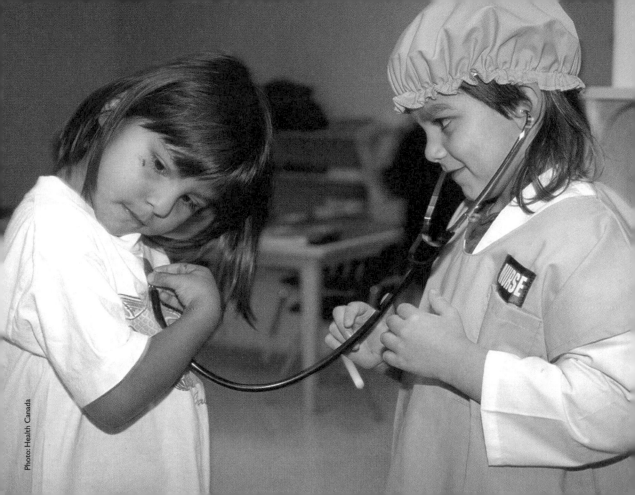

Health Care

Eye health

In the first hours of her life, a baby is given a dose of antibiotic ointment to protect her eyes from infections that she may have contracted when leaving the womb.

An infection may nonetheless occur in the subsequent weeks, indicated by:

- red or swollen eyelids;
- yellowish secretions;
- sticky eyelids;
- difficulty opening the eyes and looking at light.

Red, sticky or teary eyes

In 90% of cases, a baby or young child who has a red or sticky eye has an infection, which may be bacterial (eyelids badly swollen, pus and considerable redness), viral (very teary eyes, moderate redness) or allergic (itchy, hot or teary eyes and limited to moderate redness). The condition can also stem from the flu, a cold or a sore throat. The parents must consult an optometrist or a physician, who will prescribe the appropriate medication when necessary.

Some babies display secretions that are not yellowish but that nonetheless resemble pus. Such secretions are caused by a small defect in the opening of the canal that collects tears in the canthus, near the nose. The accumulation of tears and debris causes the secretions. The canal should, in principle, open spontaneously during the first year. Placing warm compresses on and massaging the affected area 2 or 3 times a day can soothe the baby. If the canal remains blocked, consult a physician or an optometrist.

Thrush in the mouth

White spots resembling curdled milk appear inside the mouth, on the tongue, lips and palate and on the inner lips and inside the cheeks. The spots disappear when rubbed. Your baby has thrush, which is caused by a fungus.

▶ **What to do**

Using a cotton swab dipped in a suspension of nystatin, sold by prescription, wipe the baby's mouth 4 times a day for 7 to 10 days. If you are breast-feeding, refer to the section on fungal infections in the chapter on breast-feeding, page 185.

An important reminder

- To prevent thrush: every day, wash in boiling water objects that regularly come into contact with the baby's mouth, such as nipples, pacifiers and rattles. Replace nipples and pacifiers as soon as they become sticky.
- Do not use your mouth to clean a pacifier that has fallen on the floor.

Cradle cap

Yellowish or greyish scabs appear very frequently on the scalp. The scabs take the form of scales that peel or small patches that flake off. Cradle cap is caused by excessive seborrhoeic (oil) secretions or repeated poorly rinsed shampooing. They are usually harmless but can occasionally cause itching.

▶ **What to do**

A simple shampooing may suffice. Apply the shampoo, massage the scalp and leave the shampoo on for 10 to 15 minutes to soften the scabs. Rinse thoroughly with warm water. If the situation does not improve, apply olive oil or baby oil to the scalp. Wait for several hours, then use a soft brush to remove the scales, even on the fontanel. Shampoo the scalp with warm water, rinse and dry. Repeat the treatment if the results are unsatisfactory.

If no change occurs or if the child is uncomfortable, a health professional may recommend a medicated shampoo.

Skin care

Newborns are occasionally subject to skin irritations, which are due to an array of causes.

Milium or milia

After birth, pinhead-sized white pimples may appear on the baby's forehead, nose and cheeks. They are caused by an accumulation of fatty matter in the skin pores.

▶ **What to do**

These pimples disappear within a month or 2, without treatment. Do not use oil, Vaseline, lotion or antibiotics.

Prickly heat

Prickly heat is a rash of tiny, pinpoint blisters that appear on the baby's forehead, around her neck and in the folds of her skin. This reaction occurs during hot, humid weather or when the baby has a fever. It is normal.

▶ What to do

Dress your baby lightly so that she does not sweat. If it is hot, cover her lightly. Heat rash disappears on its own in a cool environment.

Intertrigo

This type of irritation occurs when two skin surfaces come Into contact with each other, for example, under the chin, on the neck, in the armpits, on the thighs and under the scrotum. It is very important to thoroughly wash and dry these areas. The lesions appear in moist areas because of perspiration, stool or milk, which promote the development of microbes.

▶ What to do

It is essential to keep the areas clean. Wash and dry the affected areas.

Apply Vaseline or zinc oxide ointment to your baby's bottom before putting on her diaper.

Diaper rash

The baby's bottom becomes bright red and stings during urination. It is warm and painful and the child is out of sorts. Red spots appear on the bottom, the thighs, the vulva or the scrotum. Ammonia in the urine becomes corrosive on contact with the stool (see "Washing diaper," page 53). Breast-fed babies rarely have diaper rash.

Diapers usually cause diaper rash. Cotton diapers can be irritating if they are poorly rinsed or if they are not changed often enough. Some paper diapers are more irritating than others. Change brands if necessary.

However, a fungal infection can cause diaper rash, especially when the baby has thrush in the mouth. In this instance, the creams recommended to treat an irritated bottom will not eliminate the red spots.

▶ What to do

Change the diaper as soon as it is wet or soiled. Gently wash the baby's bottom with lukewarm water to which you have added a drop of olive oil. Pat the skin dry (do not rub). Repeat 3 or 4 times a day. This procedure may solve the problem.

Leave the baby's bottom uncovered. You can also expose her bottom 3 or 4 times a day to a 60-watt light bulb for 20 minutes, at a distance of 20 to 30 cm (8 to 12 inches). Be very careful: do not put the bulb closer than 20 cm (8 inches) as doing so could severely burn the child. Put a diaper under the baby's bottom to catch stools and urine.

To hasten healing, use unscented zinc oxide ointment such as zinc cream, Ihle's Paste, Desitin, Tender Age or Zincofax, or Vaseline.

Avoid overly tight diapers and plastic pants, which trap moisture and prevent air from circulating. Use disposable diaper liners. Wet towels sold in pharmacies are irritating and should only be used sparingly.

If the red spots persist after 3 or 4 days despite the application of zinc ointment, it is best to see your doctor, especially when diaper changes seem uncomfortable and the redness spreads into the folds of the skin. Your baby may have an infection.

Dry skin

Your baby's skin can become very dry, then peel or even crack.

▶ What to do

Use unscented, oil-based soap to wash your baby. Apply unscented moisturizing lotion or cream. Avoid foaming bath products. If the problem persists, consult a health professional.

Hives

Very itchy, puffy, raised red welts appear on the body. Hives are an allergic reaction to a food, virus or bacterium (see "Allergies," page 401).

▶ What to do

You must consult a doctor, who will attempt to pinpoint the cause of the hives and suggest a treatment.

Eczema or atopic dermatitis

Eczema is related to allergies (see "Allergies," page 401) and affects 5% of the population. It causes chronic lesions, which, once they have been treated, can recur. Red, scaly patches appear on the skin. Intense itching makes the child scratch herself and often makes her irritable.

In young children, the lesions occur on the face, the head, the thorax, the back of the arms and the front of the legs. They sometimes spread to folds in the neck and the knees.

Children who suffer from eczema are more susceptible than other children to becoming asthmatic.

▶ **What to do**

You must consult a doctor, who will diagnose the problem. He can then suggest the appropriate treatment, such as a lotion, cream or moisturizing ointment, for example Base Glaxal, bathing in water to which colloidal oat powder has been added, or an anti-inflammatory cream or ointment with or without cortisone.

Allergies

Allergies are a form of heightened sensitivity to normally inoffensive substances or from toxic substances.

Allergenic substances come from a wide range of sources:

- food;
- tree and plant pollen;
- animal hair;
- mould;
- dust and mites;
- pollutants, irritants and smoke from wood-burning stoves and cigarettes;
- medication and penicillin.

Allergic reactions usually affect the skin and the respiratory, digestive and ocular systems. They appear in the form of:

- hives, eczema or atopic dermatitis;
- sneezing, runny nose and asthma;
- vomiting and diarrhoea;
- red, teary eyes.

▶ What to do

Among children at high risk because of a family history of allergies, prevention is essential. Avoid allergenic substances as much as possible. However, anti-allergy vaccines are reserved for acute cases. Prolonged breast-feeding is recommended and the mother can discuss with a health professional the relevance of avoiding foods such as nuts, fish, seafood and peanuts ("Preventing allergies," page 301).

Consult a doctor, who will first pinpoint the source of the allergy before proposing a treatment.

Fever

Fever is very common during childhood. It is a normal defence against viral and bacterial infections and is not dangerous in itself. Viral infection is the main cause of fever among children and does not require antibiotics. In most instances, the fever will go away after 2 or 3 days.

A child's normal temperature varies according to the method used:

METHOD USED	NORMAL TEMPERATURE VARIATIONS
Axillary reading (armpit)	34.7°C to 37.3°C (94.5°F to 99.1°F)
Rectal reading	**36.6°C to 38.0°C (97.9°F to 100.4°F)**

A child is feverish if her temperature exceeds the normal variation, **for example, if her rectal temperature is 38.1°C (100.5°F) or more.**

It is lower early in the morning and fluctuates during the day depending on the child's activities. It is not necessary to check your baby's temperature if she is feeling fine. However, if she looks sick, is hot, red, cranky, weepy and weak, take her temperature. Make note of it in case you consult Info-Santé CLSC or your doctor.

Fever occurs when the rectal temperature exceeds 38°C (100.4°F). When a child is suffering from an infection, her temperature is unstable and it may fall or rise suddenly. The administration of medication, especially acetaminophen (see "Fever medication," page 405), will lower your child's temperature quickly.

What to use to take your baby's temperature

The best choice is a plastic electronic (digital) thermometer with digital display that doesn't contain any glass or mercury and is designed for rectal, oral or axillary (armpit) use.

The Canada Paediatric Society does not recommend the use of mercury thermometers, since accidental exposure to this toxic substance is possible if the thermometer breaks. It recommends instead an unbreakable plastic thermometer.

A plastic auricular thermometer, used to read the temperature in the ear, is more expensive and less reliable when used to take the temperature of young children.

Fever strips are not recommended as they are not accurate.

How to take the temperature

An electronic axillary thermometer placed in the armpit can be used to check whether a newborn or young child has a fever. If your child is under 2 years of age and you discover that she has a fever (an axillary reading over 37.3°C), confirm your reading by taking a **rectal reading**.

Rectal reading

The rectal reading is the most reliable way to take a young child's temperature.

- Wash the thermometer with cool, soapy water and rinse it.

- Cover the tip with petroleum jelly, such as Vaseline.

- Place your baby on her back with her knees bent.

- Gently insert the thermometer in the rectum to a depth of roughly 2.5 cm (1 inch).

- Hold the thermometer in place **until you hear the tone. Remove it and read the temperature.**

- Wash the thermometer.

Reading in the ear

This method is quicker but is not recommended since it is less accurate in the case of young children.

Oral reading

This method is not recommended for children under 5 years of age.

▶ What to do

When your baby's **rectal temperature** reaches **38.5°C (101.3°F)**, medication to treat fever (antipyretic) is recommended. It can also be given to a child who is feeling unwell, even if her temperature is lower.

Dress your baby lightly in an undershirt, diaper and socks. Lie her down and cover her with a sheet. To prevent dehydration, give her liquids frequently, for example milk, water or juice, depending on her age. Room temperature should not exceed 21°C (70°F).

A sponge bath is not recommended to counteract a high fever. It is stressful for a feverish child and its effectiveness is short-lived.

Fever medication

Acetaminophen and ibuprofen are the 2 classes of medications that reduce fever, although they do not combat the underlying infection. They act within 30 to 60 minutes. **Never use aspirin.**

The Canadian Paediatric Society recommends acetaminophen as the first choice because it has been in use for a long time. Ibuprofen is useful when children tolerate acetaminophen poorly or do not respond to it (see "Contraindications," page 327). **Do not give both medications. Use one or the other.**

First choice: acétaminophen

(Ex.: Atasol, Pediaphen, Pediatrix, Tempra, Tylenol and other generic products)

Acetaminophen's effectiveness usually depends on the dose. It is important to rely on the child's weight to determine the dose, that is, **15 mg per kilogram per dose to be repeated every**

4 to 6 hours up to a maximum of 5 doses per 24 hours. As a last resort, the child's age can be used to estimate the dose of acetaminophen to be administered. If need be, consult your pharmacist in order to determine the exact dose according to the formulation chosen and your child's weight.

Acetaminophen is sold in the form of drops, suspensions and tablets (see table, page 472). Suppositories are not always fully absorbed since they are often expelled from the anus. If your child does not readily tolerate oral medication, discuss the matter with your doctor.

Second choice: ibuprofen
(Ex.: Advil, Motrin and other generic products)

Ibuprofen is not recommended before the age of 6 months.

Ibuprofen's effectiveness usually depends on the dose. It is important to rely on the child's weight to determine the dose, that is, **10 mg per kilogram per dose to be repeated every 6 to 8 hours up to a maximum of 4 doses per 24 hours.** As a last resort, the child's age can be used to estimate the dose of ibuprofen to be administered.

Ibuprofen is sold in the form of drops, suspensions and tablets. A word of caution: the concentration of ibuprofen varies depending on the formulation (see table, page 473). Rely on the child's **weight** to determine the correct dose.

Contraindications

Ibuprofen must also be avoided when the child is suffering from severe gastroenteritis, chickenpox, asthma, kidney failure and 10 days before and 10 days after surgery. If your child has health problems, consult your doctor or pharmacist before giving her ibuprofen.

An important reminder

Keep drugs in their original containers and use childproof caps (available from a pharmacy). Keep thermometers out of the reach of children. Store them in a locked cupboard equipped with a safety latch.

What if your child throws up the dose?

If your child throws up less than 30 minutes after taking the medication, do not give her another dose. Wait 1 hour, take her temperature again and if she still has a fever, give her the same dose. If your child vomits again, do not repeat the dose; promptly consult your doctor.

When should you consult a doctor?

A high fever does not necessarily indicate serious illness. Above all, you must consider the child's overall state of health, behaviour and any other symptoms. **It is normal for a feverish child to be more inclined to cling to you and to lose her appetite.**

Contact the Info-Santé CLSC nurse or a doctor if your child is feverish and displays any of the following symptoms. The health professional can determine whether the child should be examined by a doctor.

Seek advice if your child:

- drinks little;
- vomits;
- is hard to console or cranky;
- has a persistent cough;

- has both a fever and rash;

- the fever persists for more than 48 hours for no apparent reason.

However, promptly consult a doctor (see "An important reminder," page 315) if the child is feverish and:

- is under 6 months of age;

- is vomiting a lot (see "Gastroenteritis," page 418);

- is hard to wake up;

- is pale or her colouring is poor;

- reacts little to others;

- is wheezing;

- temperature exceeds 41.1°C (106°F).

Febrile seizures

Fever can cause febrile seizures in 2 to 5% of children between the ages of 6 months and 5 years. The child loses consciousness and is subject to convulsions, which are alarming for parents but are usually harmless to the child. They last from several seconds to 15 minutes, occasionally longer, and normally cease of their own accord.

▶ **What to do**

If your child suffers a seizure, stay calm: turn her head to the side in case she vomits. Do not put anything in her mouth. An Info-Santé CLSC nurse can offer guidance by telephone. Then, see your doctor.

Upper respiratory tract infections

Upper respiratory tract infections include colds, the flu, stuffed nose, sore throat, coughs, earaches and bronchitis. They occur frequently in children up to the age of 4 years.

If your child has already suffered from an upper respiratory tract infection, as soon as you notice secretions from her nose, it is important to clean the nose with a saline solution once or twice a day. To better protect children at risk, otorhinolaryngologists recommend cleaning the nose daily (see "Stuffed nose," page 411). When the child has a cold, repeat the procedure several times a day or as needed.

Colds and the flu

The older your baby gets, the more contact she will have with other children. Her immune system is developing and she is liable to catch whatever is going around. It is normal for her to catch upper respiratory tract infections, especially colds and the flu.

▶ **What to do**

A child with a cold or the flu should drink plenty of fluids to liquefy the secretions. Maintain the room temperature at 21°C (70°F), no more. Try to lower your baby's fever (see "Fever," page 402). Take her temperature every 4 to 6 hours.

Air your baby's room. Keep stuffed toys and pets away from your child as she may be allergic to them. Do not smoke in the house.

HOW TO DISTINGUISH BETWEEN A COLD AND THE FLU

	COLD	FLU
CAUSES	Various respiratory viruses	Influenza virus
SYMPTOMS		
Fever	Mild (38°C - 39°C) (100.4°F - 102.2°F)	38°C - 40°C (100.4°F - 104°F)
Headache	Rare	Pronounced
Chills	Pronounced	Pronounced
Muscular aches	Mild	Pronounced, may be acute
Fatigue, weakness	Mild	Pronounced
Stuffed nose	Often	Occasionally
Runny nose	Pronounced	Occasionally
Sneezing	Pronounced	Occasionally
Sore throat	Pronounced	Occasionally
Cough	Mild to moderate	Heavy
Chest pains	Mild to moderate	Pronounced
INCUBATION PERIOD	1 to 3 days	
INFECTIOUSNESS	24 hours prior to and up to 5 days after the appearance of symptoms	
TRANSMISSION	Through contact with secretions from the nose and throat, sneezing, coughing, kissing and contaminated objects	
DURATION	5 to 7 days	Over 7 days
TREATMENT	No specific treatment	If type A flu or complications
COMPLICATIONS	Otitis, sinusitis	Otitis, bronchitis, pneumonia

Wash your hands thoroughly after changing her diaper and after wiping her nose. Immediately discard used paper tissues.

Prevention

Teach your child to cough or sneeze into the crook of her arm and not in her hands. Adults should do the same. This is an excellent preventive measure.

Stuffed nose

If your child's nose is obstructed by secretions, it is very important to clean her nose as often as necessary and especially before feeding and bedtime. The use of a saline solution is recommended to clean the nose, available from a pharmacy in a small bottle with a dropper. When the bottle is empty, you can prepare your own saline solution at home.

▶ **What to do**

Here is how to clean your child's nose.

- Lay your child on her back.
- Apply 1 full dropper (1 mL) of saline solution in each nostril.
- Use a cotton swab (Q-tips) to clean inside the nostrils.
- Apply another full dropper of saline solution in each nostril.
- Wipe the child's nose and encourage her to breathe through her nose if possible.

Otorhinolaryngologists recommend this technique once a day as a preventive measure for children suffering from otitis, rhinitis and sinusitis. When the child has a cold or an upper respiratory tract infection, repeat the procedure 3 or 4 times a day. Avoid any other medication when your child is under 1 year old, except as advised by a doctor.

Saline solution for the nose:
Add 2.5 mL ($\frac{1}{2}$ level teaspoon) of salt, never more, to 240 mL (8 oz.) of cooled boiled water. **It is important to measure the quantities accurately.**

◪ Handy hint

To teach your child how to blow her nose, encourage her to:

• blow bubbles with her nose in the bath;

• blow through her nose to move a cotton ball across the table (close your child's mouth with your hand).

Coughing

Coughing enables the body to expel secretions from the respiratory tract. It is a symptom of an infection in the respiratory tract, that is, the nose, the throat and the ears, usually caused by a virus.

Coughing can also be an allergic reaction (see "Allergies," page 401).

▣ What to do

Avoid giving your child cough syrup. If she is feverish and looks unwell or has trouble breathing, see a doctor.

Sore throat (pharyngitis, tonsillitis)

A sore throat is an infection of the pharynx and the tonsils that is accompanied by fever, swelling and sensitivity in the lymph nodes in the neck and, occasionally, nausea and vomiting. It is painful for the child to swallow, which leads to a reduction in the amount of milk consumed.

A throat swab enables the doctor to determine whether the infection is viral or bacterial. In 80 to

90% of cases, a virus causes it, for which there is no treatment. If bacteria cause it, usually streptococcus, antibiotics will be prescribed. When a rash accompanies the sore throat, the child may have scarlet fever (see "Scarlet fever," page 434).

Pharyngitis is transmitted through direct contact with secretions from the nose and throat of the infected individual when the latter coughs and sneezes. It can recur and there is no vaccine against it.

▶ What to do

See a doctor, who will diagnose the problem. You can give your baby acetaminophen to help bring down her temperature and relieve the pain (see "Fever medication," page 405). Ice cream and frozen juice sticks will alleviate the pain in the throat. Give your child plenty to drink. It is important to wash your hands and the baby's toys. Immediately discard used paper tissues.

Acute otitis media

Acute otitis media is an inflammation of the middle ear that may or may not be accompanied by discharges. Several days before, the child may have a runny nose. Bacteria or a virus cause otitis, which often occurs after a bad cold. It primarily affects children between the ages of 6 months and 2 years, especially in the fall and winter.

Your baby touches her ear, rolls her head on the pillow, cries, and no longer eats. She may vomit and have diarrhoea. She may or may not be feverish.

Otitis is not contagious, but colds are transmitted readily from one child to another and create a suitable environment for the disease.

▶ What to do

Give your baby acetaminophen to help bring down her temperature and relieve the pain (see "Fever medication," page 405). Frequently give her liquids. Clean her nose with a saline solution (see "Stuffed nose," page 411).

See a doctor if your baby cries a lot, is irritable, wakes up at night, or has a fever.

Once otitis has been diagnosed, antibiotics are often necessary. They prevent complications. It is important to give the full course of antibiotics even if the child seems better. In this way, she is less likely to develop resistance to treatment. Repeated, untreated middle ear infections can lead to **hearing problems**. If drainage is necessary, tubes will be put into the ear.

Prevention

Breast-fed babies are less susceptible to otitis. Nasal hygiene is also very important (see "Stuffed nose," page 411). To prevent otitis, do not put your baby to bed with a bottle since the liquid could run into the middle ear. Hold her to give her the bottle and raise her head.

Other forms of otitis

A serum-like liquid may persist behind the eardrum after a case of acute otitis media, and is known as **serous otitis media**, which can impair hearing and last for several weeks. Serous otitis usually goes away on its own and does not require treatment.

Swimmer's otitis is an infection of the external auditory canal, which becomes swollen, red and painful. You must consult your doctor.

Bronchiolitis

Bronchiolitis affects the bronchioles, small canals that allow air to circulate in the lungs. It often stems from the microbes that cause colds, especially the respiratory syncytial virus, and mainly affects children under the age of 1 year. It is one of the most frequent diseases among children up to the age of 2 years.

Coughing, a runny nose and a mild fever are the most common symptoms. Sometimes, the inside of the bronchi swell up and produce secretions. Constricted airflow causes the individual to wheeze.

The virus is highly contagious and is transmitted through coughing and contact with infected secretions. For this reason, it is important to teach children to cough into the crook of their arm and wash their hands frequently.

▶ What to do

As is true of colds, there are few effective remedies for bronchiolitis. However, some treatments can help a child cope with the illness. If need be, put a saline solution in her nostrils to free her nose of secretions (see "Stuffed nose," page 411). To ease your child's breathing, raise the head of her bed roughly 30° by sliding a pillow under the mattress. Do not put your baby directly on the pillow.

Do not use a humidifier or give your child cough syrup.

See a doctor if you think that your child's condition is deteriorating, especially if she is under the age of 6 months. Symptoms such as faster breathing, difficulty eating, coughing or breathlessness while nursing may warrant consulting a doctor.

Bronchiolitis is not necessarily a precursor of asthma. However, talk to your doctor about it if you are concerned.

Prevention

Breast-feeding is one good means of prevention. Avoid all contact with second-hand smoke from cigarettes, wood-burning stoves, and so on. Teach your children to cough into the crook of their arm and to wash their hands often. Children in day care are at greater risk between December and March.

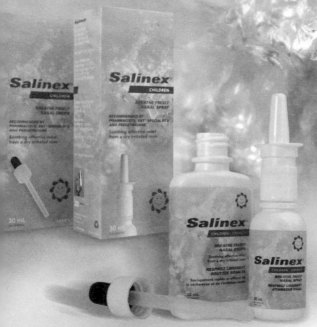 

Nasal hygiene
Application instructions

Salinex

Child under 2 years or unable to blow its nose properly

1. Lay the child on its back, head straight.
2. Apply the contents of 1 full dropper of Salinex to each nostril.
3. Clean the inside of the nostrils with a cotton swab.
4. Repeat application of 1 full dropper to each nostril.
5. Children over 2 years: seat the child with its head bent slightly forward and help the child to blow its nose, one nostril at a time.
6. These instructions may be used for daily nasal hygiene. For children suffering from colds, earaches, rhinitis and sinusitis, use as recommended by a physician.

Child able to blow its nose properly

1. Seat the child on a chair, head facing forward and ask the child to look you in the eyes (to avoid wrinkling the nose).
2. Spray each nostril with Salinex according to recommended dosage, ask the child to tilt its head forward slightly and blow its nose, one nostril at a time.
3. In the case of nasal secretions, repeat the cycle of sprays in each nostril until the secretions stop (air flow).
4. Clean the inside of the nostrils with a cotton swab as needed, and ask the child to blow its nose again, one nostril at a time.
5. These instructions may be used for daily nasal hygiene. For children suffering from colds, earaches, rhinitis and sinusitis, use as recommended by a physician.

Salinex® : an aqueous solution containing 9 mg/mL of sodium chloride

An important reminder

If your child has an upper respiratory tract infection:

- avoid smoking in your home and car. Cigarette smoke and smoke from wood fires irritate the respiratory tract;
- eliminate all products that could trigger an allergic reaction, such as carpets and plush toys, and keep domestic animals away from your child;
- if your child has gotten over otitis, check to make sure that she can hear properly. Monitor her reactions to noise, music and a small bell.

Intestinal disorders

Your child does not look sick but her stool has been liquid for a day or 2. Perhaps she has an intestinal disorder.

▶ **What to do**

Check whether your child is drinking too much juice or overly sweet liquids. Up to the age of 2 years, 60 to 90 mL (2 to 3 oz.) of juice a day is sufficient. Avoid soft drinks and limit prune juice, which contain laxative substances. Reduce quantities of cold foods such as milk, juice, ice cream, frozen treats and slush. If your child is drinking a lot of cow's milk, give her whole (3.25%) milk and limit the quantity to 600 or 725 mL (20 or 25 oz.) a day.

Do you suspect that a food recently introduced into your child's diet has caused the intestinal disorder? If so, stop giving it to her for several weeks. Try the food again later. Over time, intolerance to food disappears.

Make sure your child eats a balanced diet (see the chapter on solid foods, page 240). If she is eating enough, gaining weight and in good health, there is no reason for concern. Intestinal sensitivity may be part of her nature. However, if the situation worries you, consult a health professional.

Gastroenteritis

When a child's stools suddenly become very liquid, she is suffering from enteritis. If she also vomits, she has gastroenteritis.

Gastroenteritis is one of the most common childhood complaints. Very few children escape at least 1 bout of it during their first year. Breast-fed babies suffer less frequently from it since breast milk has a preventive, therapeutic effect. However, attending day care increases the risk.

The child's stools are more frequent and more liquid than usual and occasionally contain blood. She may also vomit or have a fever. She looks sick, is irritable or drowsy and has little appetite. Simply put, she is feeling out of sorts. In most instances, a virus causes the disease. There is no medication to cure it and diarrhoea goes away without antibiotics within several hours or from 2 to 5 days.

Dehydration is the main risk when a child has gastroenteritis, as the body loses too much water. Children under the age of 1 year are at greater risk than older children. Imbalance can occur in the electrolytes, the concentration of mineral salts in the blood.

The main signs of dehydration are:

- drowsiness;
- dry mouth, thirst;
- dark shadows under the eyes or hollow eyes;
- a sunken fontanel;
- less frequent urination and darker-than-normal urine.

If your child shows signs of dehydration, you must consult a doctor promptly.

▷ What to do

It is important for your child to drink regularly to prevent dehydration. **For breast-fed babies, breast-feeding is the best treatment. Brief, frequent feedings will help her get better.** It is sometimes necessary to give an electrolytic solution to a breast-fed child who refuses to nurse. Suspend a bottle-fed baby's commercial infant formula and replace it with 5 to 20 mL (1 to 4 teaspoons) of electrolytic solution every 5 to 10 minutes until the vomiting stops.

When vomiting has ceased for 4 to 6 hours, the baby can resume drinking commercial infant formula. Suspending commercial infant formula for more than 12 hours is not recommended. Even if the diarrhoea persists, your child can eat small amounts of the foods that are part of her usual diet. It is essential to give her limited amounts of food spread over 5 or 6 small meals to avoid the recurrence of nausea.

After 24 hours, reintroduce the other foods that are part of your child's usual diet.

Electrolytic solutions

The electrolytic solution replaces the water and mineral salts lost in the stools or through vomiting. Your pharmacy sells electrolytic solutions such as Pedialyte or Pediatric Electrolyte, and Gastrolyte, a powder sold in individual packets to be reconstituted. The Canadian Paediatric Society recommends that parents keep an electrolyte solution on hand to treat diarrhoea, as it often occurs among young children.

If the gastroenteritis begins during the night, you have no electrolytic solution at home and a pharmacy is not accessible, you can, **under exceptional circumstances**, prepare an oral rehydration solution at home. For a very short time (until the pharmacy opens), this solution can be used provided that the recipe is followed rigorously. When the recipe is not prepared properly, it can cause serious dehydration problems and imbalance the electrolytes in the blood.

The Canadian Paediatric Society advises against homemade oral rehydration solutions because serious mistakes in their preparation have been reported.

As soon as the pharmacy opens, it is important to purchase an electrolytic solution (ex. Pedialyte, etc.).

Homemade electrolytic solution

For exceptional use only until your pharmacy opens. We do not recommend using a homemade solution for longer than 12 hours. Follow these instructions carefully.

Unsweetened ready-to-drink orange juice:
360 mL (12 oz.)

Cooled boiled water:
600 mL (20 oz.)

Salt:
2.5 mL ($^1/_2$ level teaspoon), never more

Use a measuring spoon and a measuring cup to ensure that the quantities are exact. Mix the ingredients well.

How to hydrate your child

The amounts given in 1 hour depends on the child's age and are indicated below.

Under 6 months: 30 to 90 mL (1 to 3 oz.)
6 to 24 months: 90 to 125 mL (3 to 4 oz.)
Over 24 months: 125 to 250 mL (4 to 8 oz.)

If vomiting persists, reduce the amount. During the acute phase, some babies tolerate only 5 mL (1 teaspoon) at a time.

Examples of treatment

First case: the child has diarrhoea but is not vomiting or hardly vomiting

She is being fed milk only

In the case of a **breast-fed baby**, continue breast-feeding as usual. Breast milk hastens recovery from diarrhoea. If you notice that your child is drinking less milk, offer her the breast frequently.

In the case of a **bottle-fed baby**, alternate between her usual milk and a commercial electrolytic solution.

The baby is breast-fed or bottle-fed and is eating solid food

Proceed as indicated above with respect to milk. Give the baby her usual food, such as cereal, fruit and vegetable purées. Cooked, mashed rice appears to have a useful therapeutic effect.

Second case: the child has diarrhoea and is vomiting a lot

In the case of a **breast-fed baby**, continue breast-feeding but stop solid foods for roughly 4 hours. Offer your child shorter, more frequent feedings. If the child is not nursing properly, give her 5 to 10 mL (1 to 2 teaspoons) of electrolytic solution every 5 to 10 minutes, using a teaspoon or a medicine dropper.

In the case of a **bottle-fed baby**, stop the usual foods (milk and solid foods) for roughly 4 hours. Every 5 to 10 minutes, give her 5 to 10 mL (1 to 2 teaspoons) of electrolytic solution, using a teaspoon or a medicine dropper.

When vomiting subsides and your child is feeling better, increase the quantity of liquid little by little. Gradually resume feeding with her usual milk and solid foods.

When to see a doctor

This treatment usually works. If the child continues to vomit frequently and if you notice signs of dehydration, consult a doctor quickly.

An important reminder

- When your child has gastroenteritis, do not give her liquids such as apple juice (even diluted) or 7-Up (even flat) as they can aggravate the diarrhoea and unbalance the mineral salts in her body. Only the electrolytic solutions proposed earlier can help your child get better.

- Despite the bland taste of electrolytic solutions, dehydrated children drink them eagerly as dehydration causes intense thirst. If your child refuses the solution, it is usually because she is not dehydrated or thirsty. Do not add anything to enhance the taste.

Doing so would disturb the sugar-salt balance, which is essential for the success of the treatment.

- A change in your child's milk during moderate gastroenteritis is not recommended, nor is a soy-based formula, unless recommended by a doctor. Avoid lactose-free formulas as they are not useful in curing moderate gastroenteritis.

- A return to normal food within 4 to 12 hours promotes recovery from diarrhoea. An entirely liquid diet (without milk or solid food) may last from 6 to 12 hours, but **never more than 18 hours**.

A medical consultation is essential for any baby under the age of 6 months who vomits and has diarrhoea. The following signs also warrant consulting a doctor:

- your child is urinating very little;
- her mouth is dry;
- her fontanel is sunken;
- she cries without tears;
- she seems weak and drowsy;
- there is blood in her stools;
- her stools are black;
- diarrhoea has persisted for more than 5 days.

The doctor may order a fecal culture to pinpoint the bacteria or parasites responsible for the disease.

Do not give your child any medication sold in a pharmacy without first getting medical advice.

Prevention: wash your hands

Washing your hands thoroughly with soap is the most important hygiene measure against the transmission of infections.

You cannot avoid microbes. Scarcely have you finished soaping your hands and already you start to accumulate them by opening doors, wiping faces, handling children's toys and changing diapers.

However, you can reduce the possibility of infecting other people by knowing when to wash your hands, that is, before and after activities where there is a high risk of transmission.

Parents

You must wash your hands:

BEFORE preparing meals, eating, breast-feeding, feeding a child or giving her medication;

AFTER going to the toilet, including taking a child to the toilet or changing your baby's diaper; after caring for someone who is sick or (if possible) wiping someone's nose; after touching pets and cleaning an animal's cage or litter.

How to wash your hands

- Wet your hands under running water.
- Rub them with bar or liquid soap while counting up to 5.
- Rinse under running water while counting up to 5.
- Dry your hands with a clean towel.
- Use hand cream, if need be, to prevent chapping.

Children

Remember to wash your children's hands as often as necessary:

BEFORE eating or playing in water;

AFTER a diaper change or going to the toilet; after playing outdoors in sand or with animals.

How to wash your children's hands

- First wipe them with a clean cloth or paper towel thoroughly soaked in warm water and soap.
- Rinse them with another towel soaked in warm water.
- Dry them well.

Infectious Diseases

If you never gave chickenpox a second thought... Think again.

Before your child turns one year-old...
Talk to your health-care professional
about VARIVAX® III or
Visit our website at **www.varivax.ca**

VARIVAX® III is used for vaccination against chickenpox in individuals 12 months of age and older.

®Registered Trademark of Merck & Co., Inc. Used under license.

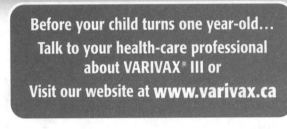

VARIVAX®
[varicella virus vaccine, live, attenuated (Oka/Merck)]

MERCK FROSST
Discovering today
for a better tomorrow.

VACCINE DIVISION
MERCK FROSST CANADA LTD.
KIRKLAND, QUEBEC

PAAB

VRV-02-CDN-84090270-JA

Microbes – viruses, bacteria, parasites or fungi – cause infectious diseases. Vaccination is an extremely effective way of protecting against several serious infections, especially in the case of children under 1 year of age. As a result of vaccination, measles, rubella (German measles) and mumps have become very rare in North America. Today's most common infectious diseases are pertussis (whooping cough), chicken pox, roseola, and scarlet fever.

Several factors explain why infectious diseases persist. Vaccines have still not been found against some diseases; parents neglect vaccination, refuse it or only partially submit to it; vaccines are not 100% effective; and not all of them are offered free of charge (this is true of chicken pox [Varivax III, Varilrix] and pneumococcus [Prevnar] vaccines).

In most instances, you must consult a doctor, who will establish a diagnosis and prescribe a treatment, if need be.

This section focuses on only a few infectious diseases that affect children up to the age of 2 years. They are presented in alphabetical order.

Chicken pox

Chicken pox is a very common, highly contagious disease that is **usually caught only once** and provides long-term immunization. The virus that causes it is transmitted directly, person to person. Children under 6 months of age rarely catch the disease, which is usually benign when caught during childhood, except by newborns. It is more serious among adolescents and adults. The streptococcus sometimes causes skin infections in the wake of the disease.

There are 2 vaccines (Varivax III and Varilrix) that can be administered to children starting at the age of 1 year. They are available in certain medical clinics and CLSCs but the ministère de la Santé et des Services sociaux does not offer the vaccine free of charge.

Incubation period: 10 to 21 days (14 to 16 days, on average).

Contagiousness: 1 to 4 days before and up to 6 days after the first spots burst.

Development: The beginning of the illness often passes unnoticed. Your child will develop a slight temperature (38°C or 100.4 °F). A rash appears followed by blisters that quickly spread all over the body. The blisters are filled with a clear fluid. They burst and scabs form over the spots. The rash causes itching. New lesions appear for 3 or 4 days and become scabby by roughly the seventh day.

Duration: 7 to 10 days.

▶ **What to do**

Give your child acetaminophen (see "Fever medication," page 405) to bring down his fever. Do not give your child aspirin or ibuprofen. Give him plenty of fluids such as water, milk or fruit juice. Try to keep your child from scratching himself by giving him mittens to wear or cutting his fingernails short. Bathe him in warm water containing colloidal oat flour (Aveeno) or 50 to 60 mL (3 or 4 tablespoons) of baking soda.

A child suffering from benign chicken pox can return to day care or school as soon as he is well enough to participate normally in activities, regardless of the state of the blisters.

Since chicken pox sometimes leads to complications, consult a doctor if any of the following situations arise:

- the child's temperature has exceeded 38.5°C (101.3°F) for more than two days;
- the fever resumes several days after the disease begins;
- spots grow bigger, turn red or become painful;
- the child seems very sick;
- he coughs or has difficulty breathing.

Measles – Mumps – Rubella

Vaccination has made these 3 infectious diseases relatively rare in Canada and Quebec.

Meningitis

Bacteria or a virus cause meningitis.

Haemophilus influenzae **type b bacterial meningitis** (Hib) is the type against which children in Quebec are vaccinated starting at the age of 2 months. It is transmitted through the secretions (coughing, sneezing) of an infected person or through contact with objects or hands contaminated by the secretions. This meningitis mainly affects children under the age of 3 years. However, the introduction of Hib vaccine, a component of Pentacel vaccine, has more or less eliminated the disease.

A massive vaccination program against **meningococcal meningitis** was conducted in Quebec in 1992, 1993 and 2001. Since 2002, the vaccine has been integrated into the vaccination schedule when children reach the age of 12 months (Menjugate or Neis Vac-C).

Pneumococcus, which responds well to antibiotics administered early, is the main cause of bacterial meningitis in older children. It can be prevented by the administration of Prevnar vaccine, for which parents must pay, since the vaccine is still not free of charge in Quebec (April 2004), except in rare instances.

Viral meningitis is often benign. Various viruses cause the disease, for which there is no specific treatment. It usually clears up without further problems.

Symptoms: Fever, drowsiness, stiffness in the neck, loss of appetite, vomiting, and irritability.

▶ What to do

See your doctor immediately. Treatment with antibiotics of bacterial meningitis is usually very effective if started early enough.

Pertussis (whooping cough)

Bacteria cause whooping cough, an infectious disease that is especially serious in children under the age of 1 year. It is transmitted through direct contact with secretions from the nose or throat of an infected individual. It can only be caught once. Whooping cough can be prevented through vaccination, although it is not 100% effective.

Incubation period: 7 to 10 days.

Contagiousness: Whooping cough is contagious during the few days that precede the fever and up to 5 days after the beginning of treatment with antibiotics. If left untreated, it remains contagious up to 3 weeks after the first coughing fits.

Development: It begins like a cold, with mild fever, around 38°C (100.4°F), and is accompanied by very heavy coughing fits that occur suddenly (the child coughs constantly). After a coughing fit, the child may have trouble catching his breath for several seconds, and when he does, may sound like a rooster crowing. The coughing can lead to vomiting and can persist for 6 to 10 weeks.

Duration: 1 to 3 months.

▶ **What to do**

See a doctor, who will prescribe antibiotics, which, if they are administered early, can reduce the seriousness of the disease and its contagiousness. If your child is choking, put him on his stomach and pat him gently on the back.

Frequently offer him liquids. Do not expose your child to cigarette smoke. See your doctor again if breathing problems occur during the illness.

Exclusion from day care: up to 5 days after the beginning of treatment with antibiotics.

Roseola
(*exanthema subitum*)

Roseola is a contagious viral infection that occurs in children between the ages of 3 months and 2 years. It starts with a high fever that lasts 3 to 5 days, then drops suddenly. A pinkish rash then appears on the face, neck and trunk. It is not known how the disease is transmitted and there is no vaccine against it. It is hardly contagious and **1 bout of roseola is thought to immunize a child for life**.

Incubation period: Indeterminate, between 5 and 15 days.

Contagiousness: The child is probably contagious during the 4 days that follow the start of the fever.

Development: Once the rash appears, the child is more or less over the disease. In most instances, his general health is good.

Duration: Roughly 1 week.

▶ **What to do**

There is no specific treatment for roseola. Give your child acetaminophen (see "Fever medication," page 405) to bring down his fever, and plenty of fluids.

Scarlet fever

Scarlet fever is an infectious illness caused by streptococci, a bacterium that produces a toxin, then a sunburn-like rash. The disease usually starts as a streptococcal infection of the throat (tonsillitis). **It is possible to catch scarlet fever more than once.** It is transmitted through direct contact with droplets from the nose and throat of an infected person. There is no vaccine against the illness.

Incubation period: 1 to 3 days, the shortest period of all infectious diseases.

Contagiousness: The child is no longer contagious 24 hours after treatment with antibiotics has begun. In the absence of treatment, scarlet fever may last up to 21 days and cause serious complications. It is essential to see a doctor.

Development: The child's temperature rises to 40°C (104°F). A sore throat and painful swallowing accompany the fever. The tongue turns raspberry red. A rash appears on the neck and in folds of skin. The skin is bright red, hot and when pressed with the fingers, a white mark remains, resembling goose bumps on a pinkish background. The skin peels after 1 week.

Duration: Roughly 1 week.

▶ **What to do**

It is essential to see a doctor, who will diagnose the disease and prescribe antibiotics. Give your child acetaminophen (see "Fever medication," page 405) to bring down his fever, and plenty of liquids.

✪ **Golden rules**

- During the first 6 months, the antibodies transmitted by his mother at the time of birth protect a baby. Breast-feeding prolongs this protection.

- Washing your hands frequently will reduce the transmission of infections.

Useful Information

Resources
for Parents

Useful addresses

Emergency resources

Centre Anti-poison du Québec
1 800 463-5060
www.inspq.qc.ca/cap
Information on what to do in the event of poisoning,
downloadable brochures.

Éducation coup-de-fil
(514) 525-2573
Parents can consult professionals through this
bilingual telephone service.

Info-santé CLSC
You can find the telephone number of your CLSC
by calling Communication-Québec at 1 800 363-1363
On the Internet: www.msss.gouv.qc.ca/index.php
A nurse provides health advice 24 hours a day,
seven days a week.

La ligne parents
(514) 288-5555 / 1 800 361-5085
Bilingual telephone support for parents of children
up to the age of 18 years.

Parent help line
1 888-603-9100
www.parentsinfo.sympatico.ca
Information and support for parents.

SOS Violence conjugale
(514) 873-9010 / 1 800 363-9010
www.maisons-femmes.qc.ca/SOS.html
Bilingual telephone service accessible 24 hours a day,
seven days a week.

Professional orders

Association des Allergologues et Immunologues du Québec
(514) 350-5101
www.allerg.qc.ca

Association des Obstétriciens et Gynécologues du Québec
(514) 849-4969
www.gynecoquebec.com/

Association des Optométristes du Québec
(514) 288-6272 / 1 888 767-6786
www.aoqnet.qc.ca

Association des Orthopédagogues du Québec
(514) 374-5883
www.adoq.org

Association des Pédiatres du Québec
(514) 350-5127
www.pediatres.ca/

Ordre des Dentistes du Québec
(514) 875-8511
www.odq.qc.ca/

Ordre des Ergothérapeutes du Québec
(514) 844-5778
www.oeq.org/

Ordre des Hygiénistes dentaires du Québec
(514) 284-7639
www.ohdq.com/

Ordre des Infirmières et Infirmiers du Québec
(514) 935-2501
www.oiiaq.org

Ordre des Optométristes du Québec
(514) 499-0524
www.ooq.org

Ordre des Orthophonistes et Audiologistes du Québec
(514) 282-9123
www.ooaq.qc.ca

Ordre des Psychologues du Québec
(514) 738-1881
www.ordrepsy.qc.ca/

Ordre des Sage Femmes du Québec
(514) 286-1313

Ordre professionnel des Diététistes du Québec
(514) 393-3733
www.opdq.org/

441

Ordre professionnel des Physiothérapeutes du Québec
(514) 351-2770
www.oppq.qc.ca/

Ordre professionnel des Travailleurs sociaux du Québec
(514) 731-3925
www.optsq.org/

Government agencies

Association des CLSC et des CHSLD du Québec
(514) 931-1448
www.clsc-chsld.qc.ca/

Directeur de l'état civil – Gouvernement du Québec
www.etatcivil.gouv.qc.ca/ENGLISH/default.htm
(514) 864-3900 / (418) 643-3900 / 1 800 567-3900
Contact the Directeur de l'état civil to obtain birth certificates.

Ministère de l'Environnement du Québec
1 800 561-1616
www.menv.gouv.qc.ca/
Lists laboratories accredited to check the quality of water from private wells.

Office de la protection du consommateur – Gouvernement du Québec
1 888 672-2556
www.opc.gouv.qc.ca/

Programme provincial de dépistage urinaire – Centre hospitalier universitaire de Sherbrooke, Hôpital Fleurimont
(819) 564-5253
This bilingual service provides information on the hereditary metabolic diseases screening program available to all newborns.

Régie de l'assurance-maladie du Québec
(418) 646-4636 / 1 800 561-9749
www.ramq.gouv.qc.ca

Secrétariat à l'adoption internationale
(514) 873-5226 / 1 800 861-0246
www.msss.gouv.qc.ca/adoption
Government agency that provides information on
international adoption and a list of resources.

Associations, agencies and support groups

Also, see "Breast-feeding resources," pages 454-457.

Allergy Asthma Information Association
(514) 694-0679
www.aaia.ca
Support and information on allergies.

Anaphylaxis Canada
(416) 785-5666
www.anaphylaxis.ca
Support and information for families living with
anaphylaxis.

Association de parents pour l'adoption québécoise
(514) 990-9144
www.quebecadoption.net/
Promotes the adoption of children born in Quebec.
Support, conferences and family activities.

Association des parents d'enfants prématurés du Québec (APEP)
(514) 523-3974
www.colba.net/~apep
Information and support services for parents of
premature children.

Fédération des associations de familles monoparentales et recomposées du Québec
(514) 729-6666
www.cam.org/fafmrq
The federation defends the rights and interests of
single-parent and blended families in Quebec.
Bilingual service is available in Montréal and some
regions of Quebec.

Fédération du Québec pour le planning des naissances
(514) 866-3721
www.fqpn.qc.ca
This bilingual service provides information on
contraception and women's sexual health.

La ligne J'ARRÊTE
1 888 853-6666
Information and support to individuals who wish to stop smoking (bilingual service).

Montreal Parents' of Twins Association
(514) 630-6625
The Association helps families in Montréal who have experienced a multiple birth.

Re Père
(514) 381-3511
www.repere.org
Assistance and support program for fathers. Service in French and English.

Serena
(514) 273-7531
www.serena.ca/
Promotes natural family planning methods. Service in French and English.

Web sites

Government sites

Baby is on the Way – Communication-Québec
1 800 363-1363
www.comm-qc.gouv.qc.ca/en/guides.html
The guide *Baby is on the Way* can be downloaded in PDF.

Car Time – Transport Canada
www.tc.gc.ca/roadsafety/childsafe/cindex_e.html
This federal government site offers extensive advice on installing children's car seats and explanations concerning the seats.

Health Canada
www.hc-sc.gc.ca
Provides information on various topics related to children's health and safety.

Ministère de la Santé et des Services sociaux du Québec

www.msss.gouv.qc.ca

Information on the services and publications available from the ministère de la Santé et des Services sociaux.

Régie des rentes du Québec – Gouvernement du Québec

www.rrq.gouv.qc.ca

Information on the family allowance program.

Secure them for Life – Société de l'assurance automobile du Québec

www.saaq.gouv.qc.ca/publications/prevention/siege_an.pdf

Complete information on the installation of children's car seats and includes a link to the children's car seat verification network.

Other sites

Canadian Health Network

www.canadian-health-network.ca

Information on a broad range of topics, including the prevention of violence, injury prevention, healthy diet, and so on.

Canadian immunization awareness program

www.immunize.cpha.ca

Information on vaccines and the vaccination schedule, answers common questions and lists resources.

Canadian Institute of Child Health

www.cich.ca

Devoted to child and family health and offers parents numerous publications and resources.

Canadian Red Cross

www.redcross.ca

Information on Red Cross prevention and first aid courses for the parents of young children and on the course for babysitters.

Caring for kids – Canadian Paediatric Society

www.caringforkids.cps.ca
Information on children's health.

Child & Family Canada

www.cfc-efc.ca
Some 50 Canadian non-profit organizations offer
information on children and families.

Éditions de l'Hôpital Sainte-Justine

www.hsj.qc.ca/editions/pagehtml/fr_english.html
The hospital's publications dealing with childhood
and families listed on this site can be ordered on line.

Feeding your baby – Dietitians of Canada

www.dietitians.ca/english/frames.html
Fact sheets on breast-feeding and the diets of babies
and infants.

Info-circumcision

www.infocirc.org/index-e.htm
Documentation and professional references
concerning circumcision.

Invest in Kids Foundation

www.investinkids.ca
1 877 583-5437
Promotes the healthy development of children
up to the age of 5 years.

Is your child seated safely in your car? – CAA Québec

www.caaquebec.com/en/automobile/bebe.asp
The CAA Québec site recommends, by region,
garages whose employees have received training in
the installation of children's car seats.

Safe Kids Canada

www.securijeunescanada.com/english/home.html
Downloadable fact sheets on safety tips for children
under the age of 5 years.

Work family tips

www.infofamilleboulot.com/home_en.htm
Ideas on a broad range of topics of interest to
families, including outings, activities, care, and tips.

Suggested readings

General books and magazines

101 Ways to Raise a Happy Baby
Lisa McCourt. Illinois: Lowel House, 1999, 160 pages, $19.95.
Advice on the first 18 months of a baby's life.

Complete Book of Mother & Baby Care
Elizabeth Fenwick, in association with the Canadian Medical Association. Montréal: The Reader's Digest Association (Canada) Ltd., 1997, 256 pages, $39.95.
A practical parents' handbook from conception to three years.

Breast-feeding

Breastfeeding Pure & Simple
Gwen Gotsch. La Leche League International, 1994, 117 pages, $14.00.
Answers the full range of questions on breast-feeding. To obtain a copy, call La Leche League of Canada at 1 800 665-4324 or fill out the on-line order form on the organization's Web site (www.lalecheleaguecanada.ca/).

Womanly Art of Breastfeeding
La Leche League International Staff, 1997, 480 pages, $22.95.
Copies of this practical reference guide on breast-feeding can be obtained from La Leche League of Canada by calling 1 800 665-4324 or by filling out the on-line order form on the organization's Web site (www.lalecheleaguecanada.ca/).

Diet

Feeding your Baby the Healthiest Food.
Louise Lambert-Lagacé. Toronto: Fitzhenry & Whiteside Publishing Company, 2000, 296 pages, $20. Complete guide to the diets of newborns and young children.

Children's development

Baby Massage
Alan Heath and Nicki Bainbridge. London: Dorling Kindersley Limited, 2000, 96 pages, $21.95. This richly illustrated guide provides step-by-step explanations of baby massage.

Baby Play & Learn
Penny Warner. Minnetonka: Meadowbrook Press, 1999, 200 pages, $16.95. This book focuses on activities for young children.

Self-Esteem: A Passport for Life
Germain Duclos. Montréal: Éditions de l'Hôpital Sainte-Justine in collaboration with *Enfants Québec* magazine, 2000, 120 pages, $13.95. Suggests practical ways to help children develop a sense of self-esteem from an early age.

The Steps and Stages: from 1-3, the Toddler Years
Holly Bennet and Teresa Pitman. Toronto: Key Porter Books Limited, 1998, 136 pages, $12.95. Parents' comments and the advice of specialists concerning basic care, language learning, sharing and sociability.

Lifestyle habits

Keys to Children's Sleep Problems
Susan Gottlieb. Haupaugge: Barron's Educational Series Company, Inc., 1993, 208 pages, $8.95. Explains the sleep cycles and proposes solutions to the most common problems.

Nighttime Parenting

William Sears, MD. La Leche League International, 1992, 201 pages, $18.99.

Provides practical advice on nighttime dilemmas for parents of babies and older children. To obtain a copy, call La Leche League of Canada at 1 800 665-4324 or fill out the on-line order form on the organization's Web site (www.lalecheleaguecanada.ca/).

Specific situations

The Fussy Baby Book

William Sears, MD and Martha Sears. La Leche League International, 2002, 237 pages, $18.95. Practical advice for parents with difficult or demanding children. To obtain a copy, call La Leche League of Canada at 1 800 665-4324 or fill out the on-line order form on the organization's Web site (www.lalecheleaguecanada.ca/).

Miscellaneous publications

10 Great Reasons to Breastfeed and 10 Valuable Tips for Successful Breastfeeding – Health Canada

www.hc-sc.gc.ca/pphb-dgspsp/publications_e.html (613) 954-5995 / 1 800 622-6232

These publications on breast-feeding can be downloaded or ordered on line.

Canada's Food Guide to Healthy Eating. Focus on Preschoolers. Background for Educators and Communicators – Health Canada

www.hc-sc.gc.ca/english/index.html (click on the "Healthy Living" tab, then on "Food and Nutrition") Fact sheet on Canada's Food Guide to Healthy Eating adapted for young children.

Guides and brochures published by the ministère de l'Emploi, de la Solidarité sociale et de la Famille

www.messf.gouv.qc.ca

(514) 873-2323 / 1 800 363-0310

Publications that can be ordered by telephone

At Your Service! Families

Theme: When you live in a family, there are many things you need to know.

This guide indicates all of the government resources available to families and can be downloaded from the Web site.

Being a Father, A Great Adventure

This publication offers reflections on the new concept of fatherhood.

Right Day Care for your Child

This guide proposes a checklist to help you choose a day-care service.

Your Turn

This test helps you determine whether your family members are sharing tasks fairly.

Hand in Hand: Emergent Literacy From A to Z – Ministère de l'Éducation (MEQ)

This early-learning kit devoted to reading and writing can be obtain from the MEQ Web site at:

www.meq.gouv.qc.ca/dfga/english/subjects/default.htm

1. Click on "Literacy Training," "Other Productions and Themes," then "Hand in Hand."

Moving and Growing – Canadian Institute of Child Health

www.cich.ca/childdev.htm

This collection of three booklets ranging from 54 to 70 pages presents exercises, activities and games for children up to the age of 2 years, from 2 to 4 years of age, and 5 and 6 years of age. The booklets are $5 each or $12 for the series and can be ordered on the Web site or by calling (613) 230-8838.

The First Years Last Forever – Canadian Institute of Child Health

www.cich.ca/childdev.htm
This 12-page booklet proposes 10 guidelines to promote the healthy development of young children and prepare them to start school. It can be ordered on line or by telephone at (613) 230-8838.

The authors have chosen the organizations and references mentioned in this section because of their relevance to the users of this guide. However, the list is by no means exhaustive and neither the authors nor the Institut national de santé publique du Québec are in any way responsible for the contents of the references indicated.

Notes

Notes

Breast-feeding resources

La Leche League

Services are offered in several regions of Quebec as well as Ontario. For the phone number closest to you, call the monitor at 1 866 ALLAITER. For english service call (613) 238-5919. Or visit the Web site at www.allaitement.ca.

Nourri-Source

Services are offered in 6 regions of Quebec (Montréal, Laval, Laurentians, Lanaudière, Montérégie and Lac-St-Jean).
Fédération québécoise Nourri-Source
www.nourri-source.org

Other resources by region

Many services are provided by volunteers and are not necessarily available in English.

REGION 01 – BAS-SAINT-LAURENT

AMQUI
Nourrissons-Lait de la Vallée — (418) 631-5248

KAMOURASKA
Les p'tits Gobe-Lait — 1 866 492-2323

LA MÉTIS
Entre mères — (418) 730-3001

MATANE
Lait Douces Heures — (418) 562-5741, ext. 6281

NOTRE-DAME-DU-LAC
Lait Mères-Veillent — (418) 899-2177 or (418) 854-2572

RIMOUSKI
Entre mères — (418) 750-7001

RIVIÈRE-BLEUE
Mère-Nature — (418) 893-1082, ext. 106

RIVIÈRE-DU-LOUP
Nourrissons-Lait Rivière-du-Loup — (418) 863-7891

TROIS-PISTOLES
Les douces Mères — (418) 851-3700, ext. 590

REGION 02 – SAGUENAY-LAC-SAINT-JEAN

CHICOUTIMI
Service d'accompagnement Écoute maman — (418) 545-0886

La Leche League	(418) 696-2441

LA BAIE

Les mères veilleuses du Fjord	(418) 676-2532

SAGUENAY

La Leche League	(418) 547-0991
Aide-maman plus	(418) 547-4792

ROBERVAL

Association Éveil-naissance	(418) 275-6581

ALMA

Nourri-Source	(418) 668-4563, ext. 243

DOLBEAU-MISTASSINI

Parensemble	(418) 239-0339

REGION 03 - QUÉBEC (NATIONAL CAPITAL)

QUÉBEC-MÉTROPOLITAIN

Mamie-lait	(418) 847-1957
Chantelait	(418) 877-5333
Entraide naturo lait	(418) 688-0262
Allaitement Québec	(418) 623-0971

CHARLEVOIX

Aidons-lait	(418) 665-6413

REGION 04 - MAURICIE ET CENTRE-DU-QUÉBEC

DRUMMONDVILLE

Nourrissons-lait	(819) 478-9307
	(pager) (819) 470-5697

LA TUQUE

Entraide-Allaitement	(819) 523-4581, ext. 2147

LAURIERVILLE

Aide à la femme à l'allaitement maternel et à la maternité (AFAM)	(819) 365-4297

LOUISEVILLE

Tendre-Allaitement	(819) 228-9486, ext. 600

SAINTE-ANNE-DE-LA-PÉRADE

Maison de la Famille Des Chenaux	(418) 325-2120
	(pager) (819) 386-6583

SAINT-TITE

Maison de la Famille du GENP	(418) 365-4405
	or (418) 365-9248

SHAWINIGAN

Allaitement-Soleil	(819) 536-2018

TROIS-RIVIÈRES

Centre de ressources pour la naissance de la Mauricie	(819) 370-3822
Maison des Familles Chemin du Roi Inc.	(819) 693-7665
Maternaide du Québec	(819) 691-3181

BOIS-FRANCS

Association Parents-ressources des Bois-Francs, La Couvée	(819) 758-4041
La Leche League des Bois-Francs	(819) 225-8367

REGION 05 - ESTRIE

LAC MÉGANTIC

Maison de la famille du Granit	(819) 583-1824

SHERBROOKE

La Leche League	(819) 829-0251

Naissance-Renaissance Estrie	(819) 569-3119

REGION 06 – MONTRÉAL-CENTRE

La Leche League (francophone)	(514) 990-8917
	or 1 866 ALLAITER
La Leche League Canada (anglophone)	1 800 665-4324

MONTRÉAL
Nourri-Source-Montréal	(514) 948-5160

REGION 07 – OUTAOUAIS

ENTIRE REGION
Nourri-Lait	(819) 561-LAIT
La Leche League	(français) 1 866 255-2483
	(english) (613) 238-5919

MANIWAKI
Centre Parents-enfants de la Haute-Gatineau	(819) 441-0282

REGION 08 – ABITIBI-TÉMISCAMINGUE

La Leche League	(819) 757-2091
	or 1 866 757-2091

REGION 09 – CÔTE-NORD

SEPT-ÎLES
À la source	(418) 962-2572, ext. 4120

BAIE-COMEAU
Aimons-Lait	(418) 589-2117

REGION 10 – NORD-DU-QUÉBEC

LEBEL-SUR-QUEVILLON
Les animations Pace-Âge	(819) 755-4247

REGION 11 – GASPÉSIE-ÎLES-DE-LA-MADELEINE

CAP-AUX-MEULES
Sein-pathique	(418) 986-2572

GASPÉ
Parenfant	(418) 368-6028

PABOS
Lactescence Pabos	(418) 689-2572
	(pager) (418) 689-8172

SAINTE-ANNE-DES-MONTS
Regroupement d'entraide	(418) 763-7771, ext. 2709
à l'allaitement maternel,	or (418) 797-2744, ext. 222
Nourrisson-Lait	

FROM MATAPÉDIA TO PASPÉBIAC
Supportons-Lait	(418) 364-2572

REGION 12 - CHAUDIÈRE-APPALACHES

Allaitement-Québec	(418) 623-0971

REGION 13 – LAVAL

LAVAL
La Leche League de Laval	1 866 ALLAITER
Fédération québécoise Nourri-Source	(514) 948-5160

REGION 14 – LANAUDIÈRE

Nourri-Source Lanaudière	(450) 589-4035
	or 1 877 589-4035

SAINT-GABRIEL-DE-BRANDON

Les mères veilleuses de Cible famille Brandon	(450) 835-9094

MRC MATAWINIE

Centre mère enfant de Manawan	(819) 971-8852
Défi-famille Matawinie	(450) 886-0458
Les amies de l'allaitement de la Matawinie	(450) 882-1038

REGION 15 – LAURENTIDES

La Leche League	1 866 ALLAITER
Nourri-Source	(450) 436-2763
	toll free 1 866 436-2763

MRC ANTOINE-LABELLE

La Mère-Veille	(819) 623-3009
	or 1 866 623-3009

16 - MONTÉRÉGIE

NOURRI-SOURCE MONTÉRÉGIE (4 SUB-REGIONS)
Toll-free number through Distributel: call the Distributel number in your region, wait for the dial tone, then dial Nourri-Source Montérégie at (450) 373-2463.

Nourri-Source Haute-Yamaska-Granby 776-2000, and	(450) 373-2463
Nourri-Source Huntingdon 377-4000, and	(450) 373-2463
Nourri-Source La Presqu'Île (514) 877-5000, and	(450) 373-2463
Nourri-Source Seigneurie-de-Beauharnois	(450) 373-2463

BELŒIL

Centre Périnatal Le Berceau	(450) 446-7760

BOUCHERVILLE

CALM	(450) 449-3479

BROMONT

La Leche League Cowansville Monique Davignon	1 866 ALLAITER

BROSSARD

La mère à boire	(450) 445-4452, ext. 2435

RICHELIEU

Entraide maternelle du Richelieu	(450) 658-7561, ext. 164

SOREL

Carrefour-Naissance-Famille du Bas-Richelieu	(450) 743-0359

SAINT-CONSTANT

Amitié Matern'elle	(450) 925-1808

LONGUEUIL

MAM	(514) 990-9626

SAINT-JEAN-SUR-RICHELIEU

Les Relevailles Vallée des Forts	(450) 359-6031

SAINT-MICHEL

Lait-Source	(450) 454-4692

SAINT-HYACINTHE

La Leche League Saint-Hyacinthe	(450) 799-5363

SAINT-THÉODORE D'ACTON

La Leche League Acton	(450) 546-3332

CHÂTEAUGUAY

La Leche League Châteauguay	(450) 427-1921

Index

Notes

FEVER MEDICATION

FIRST CHOICE: ACETAMINOPHEN (Ex.: Atasol, Pediaphen, Pediatrix, Tempra, Tylenol and other generic products)

Acetaminophen's effectiveness usually depends on the dose. It is important to rely on the child's weight to determine the dose, that is, **15 mg per kilogram per dose to be repeated every 4 to 6 hours up to a maximum of 5 doses per 24 hours**. As a last resort, the child's age can be used to estimate the dose of acetaminophen to be administered. If need be, consult your pharmacist in order to determine the exact dose according to the formulation chosen and your child's weight.

WEIGHT (kg)	WEIGHT (lb.)	MAXIMUM SINGLE DOSE (mg)	SINGLE DOSE DROPS ACETAMINOPHEN ATASOL, TEMPRA, TYLENOL 80 mg / 1 mL	LIQUID ATASOL, TEMPRA (SYRUP) 80 mg / 5 mL	ACETAMINOPHEN TYLENOL (ELIXIR) 160 mg / 5 mL	CHEWABLE TABLETS** ACETAMINOPHEN TEMPRA, TYLENOL 80 mg / tablet	TEMPRA, TYLENOL (JUNIOR) 160 mg / tablet
2.5-3.9	6-8	40 mg	0.5 mL	2.5 mL	*1.25 mL	–	–
4.0-5.4	9-11	60 mg	0.75 mL	3.75 mL	*1.25 mL	–	–
5.5-6.4	12-14	80 mg	1.0 mL	5 mL	2.5 mL	I tablet	–
6.5-7.9	15-17	100 mg	1.25 mL	5 mL	2.5 mL	I tablet	–
8.0-9.0	18-20	120 mg	1.5 mL	7.5 mL	*3.75 mL	I tablet	–
9.1-10.9	21-23	140 mg	1.75 mL	7.5 mL	*3.75 mL	I tablet	–
11.0-11.9	24-26	160 mg	2.0 mL	10 mL	5.0 mL	2 tablets	I tablet
12.0-13.4	27-29	180 mg	2.25 mL	10 mL	5.0 mL	2 tablets	I tablet
13.5-14.5	30-31	200 mg	2.5 mL	10 mL	5.0 mL	2 tablets	–
14.6-15.4	32-33	220 mg	2.75 mL	10 mL	5.0 mL	2 tablets	–
15.5-15.9	34-35	240 mg	3.0 mL	15 mL	7.5 mL	3 tablets	–

* To measure this dose, it is necessary to use a graduated syringe, which you can obtain from your pharmacist.
** Crush the tablets before giving to young children to help prevent choking.

SECOND CHOICE: IBUPROFEN (Ex.: Advil, Motrin and other generic products)

Ibuprofen is not recommended before the age of 6 months. It must also be avoided when the child is suffering from severe gastroenteritis, chicken pox, asthma, kidney failure and 10 days before and 10 days after surgery. If your child has health problems, consult your doctor or pharmacist before giving her ibuprofen.

Ibuprofen's effectiveness usually depends on the dose. It is important to rely on the child's weight to determine the dose, that is, **10 mg per kilogram per dose to be repeated every 6 to 8 hours up to a maximum of 4 doses per 24 hours.** As a last resort, the child's age can be used to estimate the dose of ibuprofen to be administered.

WEIGHT (kg)	WEIGHT (lb.)	MAXIMUM DOSE (mg)	DROPS (40 mg/mL) MOTRIN: SUSPENSION AND DROPS ADVIL: PAEDIATRIC DROPS	SUSPENSION (20 mg/mL) ADVIL: SUSPENSION MOTRIN: LIQUID SUSPENSION	TABLET* (100 mg) MOTRIN	CHEWABLE TABLET* (50 mg) MOTRIN
3.0-3.9	6.6-8.6	30 mg	0.75 mL	1.5 mL	–	–
4.0-4.9	8.7-10.9	40 mg	1.0 mL	2 mL	–	–
5.0-5.9	11.0-12.9	50 mg	1.25 mL	2.5 mL	–	–
6.0-6.9	13.0-15.1	60 mg	1.5 mL	3 mL	–	–
7.0-7.9	15.2-17.4	70 mg	1.75 mL	3.5 mL	–	–
8.0-8.9	17.5-19.6	80 mg	2.0 mL	4 mL	–	–
9.0-9.9	19.7-21.8	90 mg	2.25 mL	4.5 mL	–	–
10.0-10.9	21.9-23.9	100 mg	2.5 mL	5 mL	1 tablet	2 tablets
11.0-11.9	24.0-26.1	110 mg	2.75 mL	5.5 mL	1 tablet	2 tablets
12.0-12.9	26.2-28.4	120 mg	3.0 mL	6 mL	1 tablet	2 tablets
13.0-13.9	28.5-30.6	130 mg	3.25 mL	6.5 mL	1 tablet	2 tablets
14.0-14.9	30.7-32.8	140 mg	3.5 mL	7 mL	1 tablet	2 tablets
15.0-15.9	32.9-35.0	150 mg	3.75 mL	7.5 mL	1 1/2 tablets	3 tablets
16.0-16.9	35.1-37.2	160 mg	4 mL	8 mL	1 1/2 tablets	3 tablets

* Crush the tablets before giving to young children to help prevent choking.

CONVERSION TABLE

GRAMS	OUNCES	GRAMS	POUNDS	GRAMS	POUNDS
28 grams	1 ounce	454 grams	1 pound	7,711 grams	17 pounds
57 grams	2 ounces	907 grams	2 pounds	8,165 grams	18 pounds
85 grams	3 ounces	1,361 grams	3 pounds	8,618 grams	19 pounds
113 grams	4 ounces	1,814 grams	4 pounds	9,072 grams	20 pounds
142 grams	5 ounces	2,268 grams	5 pounds	9,525 grams	21 pounds
170 grams	6 ounces	2,722 grams	6 pounds	9,979 grams	22 pounds
198 grams	7 ounces	3,175 grams	7 pounds	10,433 grams	23 pounds
227 grams	8 ounces	3,629 grams	8 pounds	10,886 grams	24 pounds
255 grams	9 ounces	4,082 grams	9 pounds	11,340 grams	25 pounds
283 grams	10 ounces	4,536 grams	10 pounds	11,793 grams	26 pounds
312 grams	11 ounces	4,990 grams	11 pounds	12,247 grams	27 pounds
340 grams	12 ounces	5,443 grams	12 pounds	12,701 grams	28 pounds
369 grams	13 ounces	5,897 grams	13 pounds	13,154 grams	29 pounds
397 grams	14 ounces	6,350 grams	14 pounds	13,608 grams	30 pounds
425 grams	15 ounces	6,804 grams	15 pounds	14,061 grams	31 pounds
454 grams	16 ounces	7,257 grams	16 pounds	14,515 grams	32 pounds

KEY
1 ounce = 28 grams
1 pound = 454 grams
1 kilogram = 1,000 grams
1 kilogram = 2.205 pounds

EXAMPLE
6 pounds 10 ounces = 3,005 grams
or 3.005 kilograms

LIQUID MEASURES
1 ounce = 30 ml
1 cup = 240 ml
1 teaspoon = 5 ml
1 tablespoon = 15 ml

To convert Fahrenheit degrees into Celsius degrees:

$$°C = \frac{(°F - 32) \times 5}{9}$$

Education!
Is there any greater gift?

By starting to save now only a few dollars every month in a Registered Education Savings Plan (RESP), you will increase his/her chances to realize his/her dreams.

In addition, take advantage of the Canada Education Savings Grant (CESG) that equals 20% of every dollar invested, up to $400 per year.

Take part in our annual contest to win a scholarship worth approximately $20,000. Simply complete and mail the entry form on the reverse side.

UNIVERSITAS FOUNDATION has been serving young families for over 40 years and is dedicated to the cause of Education!

UNIVERSITAS
FOUNDATION
OF CANADA

www.universitas.qc.ca

Your child could win up to $ 20, 000. worth in scholarships

(approximate maximum value)

Universitas Foundation of Canada Draw

DRAW WILL TAKE PLACE ON THE 2ND FRIDAY OF DECEMBER.

CAPITAL LETTERS PLEASE

NAME OF PARENT _____

ADDRESS _____ **APT.** ____

CITY _____ **PROV.** _____ **POSTAL CODE** _____

TEL./HOME (   ) _____ **TEL./OFFICE (   )** _____

OCCUPATION _____

E-MAIL _____

Name of child _____

REGISTERED EDUCATION SAVINGS PLAN
(less than 10 years of age on the day of draw)

Date of birth: _____ _____ _____
            day   month   year

UNIVERSITAS
FOUNDATION
OF CANADA

3005, Maricourt Ave
Sainte-Foy (Quebec)
G1W 4T8

Acknowledgements

For more than 25 years now, many professionals have added their expertise and support to each issue of this guide. Our special thanks go to everyone involved in updating the 2005 edition.

Establishments in the health and social services network and organizations: Association des CLSC et des CHSLD du Québec, Association pour la santé publique du Québec, Centre Anti-poison, Centre de médecine génétique du Québec, Direction de santé publique de Québec, de Lanaudière, de la Montérégie et de Montréal, Hôpital Sainte-Justine, Info-médicaments, Les Publications du Québec, Programme provincial des protocoles infirmiers Info-Santé CLSC, Société de l'assurance automobile du Québec, Le comité des pères de Cible Famille Brandon.

Individuals: Marie-Josée Allie, Suzanne Atkinson, Jean-Louis Auger, Dalal Badlissi, Claude Bégin, Martine Bienvenue, Georges Bolduc, Josée Bussières, Antoine Chapdeleine, Louise Condrain, Maurice Coutu, Nicole Desjardins, Marie-France Desrosiers, Suzanne Dionne, Dominique Doré, Danielle Durand, Luc Ferland, Suzanne Forgues, Daniel Fortier, David Fortier, Cécile Fortin, Annie Fournier, Jean-Pierre Gauthier, Sophie Gaudreau, Isabelle Gignac, Johanne Godet, Sophie Gravel, Gloria Jeliu, Jean-Pierre Lagacé, Michel Lavoie, Stéphanie Ledoux, Luc Legris, Pierre Lévesque, Micheline Maltais, Jocelyne Martel, Louise Mathers, Yves Michaud, Jean-Luc Nadon, Martine Pageau, France Paradis, Manon Parisien, Chantale Pelletier, Julie Poissant, Richard Pelland, Luc Plante, Marie-Claude Quintal, Guy Sanfaçon, Marie-Josée Santerre, Monique Séguin, Monik St-Pierre, Emmanuelle Raynal, Céline Richard, France Richard, Daniel Roy, Hélène Tremblay, Roch Tremblay, Julie Trudel, Josée Turcotte.

We would also like to thank all those whose comments and questions have helped make this a better guide over the years. Your contributions are invaluable to our annual updates to the guide's contents.

Many thanks also to the parents who use this guide and return the attached questionnaire (page 478) to us.

Sponsors that have made possible the distribution free of charge of this book between 1977 and 2005

| Ministère de la Santé et des Services sociaux | Institut national de santé publique |
| Québec | Québec |

| 1977 to 1993 | 1994 to 1999 | 1980 to 2005 | 2000 to 2005 |

Advertising partners in the 1988 to 2005 editions

The 18 Quebec regional health and social services boards: 1998 to 2005

Bas-Saint-Laurent ▪ Saguenay–Lac-Saint-Jean ▪ National Capital ▪ Mauricie–Centre-du-Québec ▪ Estrie ▪ Montréal ▪ Outaouais ▪ Abitibi-Témiscamingue ▪ Côte-Nord ▪ Nord-du-Québec ▪ Gaspésie–Îles-de-la-Madeleine ▪ Chaudière-Appalaches ▪ Laval ▪ Lanaudière ▪ Laurentides ▪ Montérégie ▪ Nunavik ▪ Terres-Cries-de-la-Baie-James ▪

Tell us what you think

To maintain a tradition of scientific rigour and ensure ease of use, we ask you, the users of *From Tiny Tot to Toddler*, to share with us your comments and your expectations concerning the 2006 edition of the guide. Please fill out the evaluation form below and send it to:

Institut national de santé publique du Québec
From Tiny Tot to Toddler
500, boul. René-Lévesque Ouest, bureau 9.100
Montréal (Quebec) H2Z 1W7
Fax: (514) 864-1616
E-mail: pascale.turcotte@inspq.qc.ca

Please feel free to share additional comments in a separate letter and return it with this form. Thank you!

1 Has this guide been useful to you? In what way?
_____
_____

2 Are there any topics or key themes that you would like to have added to the guide? Which ones?
_____
_____

3 Are any of the topics or explanations unclear?
_____
_____

4 Would you like more extensive suggestions on books, videocassettes, useful addresses or other sources of information? If so, please specify:
_____
_____

5 Are you replying as (please check the appropriate answer):
○ a parent?
○ someone who works in the health and social services or day-care services networks?
○ other?

Send us your best photos and help illustrate an invaluable resource for parents!

Address your photos in electronic form to pascale.turcotte@inspq.qc.ca

We need your authorization to publish your photos. Please complete the permission form, which you can find on our Web site at www.inspq.qc.ca/MieuxVivre

Fax the form with a short description of the photo to (514) 864-1616.

We would like to thank our advertising partners for their valuable contribution, making the distribution of this new 2005 edition possible.

Yoplait	First insert	Yogurt and reference sheet for telephone numbers
Coppertone	Cover 3	Prevention advice and tips on using sunscreen to protect children's skin from the sun
Groupe Jean-Coutu	Cover 4	Assistance and advice from Jean-Coutu pharmacists
Éduc-alcool	page 4	*La grossesse et l'alcool en questions* brochure
Association des optométristes du Québec	page 39	Eye exams for young children
Boutique La Mère Hélène	page 52	Cotton diaper specialists
Grolier	Insert	Children's books and offer of three free books
Clément	page 117	Discount on the purchase of children's clothing and accessories
Stérilets	page 128	Sterilet as a contraception technique
Ordre Professionnel des Diététistes du Québec	page 178	For a healthy diet from birth
Réseau québécois des accompagnantes à la naissance	page 195	Support before, during and after the birth
Medela	page 199	Breast milk extraction; 3 models of breast pumps
Souris Mini	page 237	Children's clothing and coupon for free body suit
La mère poule	page 264	Frozen foods for babies
Industrielle-Alliance Insurance and financial services	Insert	Free accident insurance for 12 months
Dorel	page 361	Alpha Omega Elite 3-in-1 convertible car seat
SABEX	page 391	Saline solution recommended for cleaning a blocked nose
SABEX	Insert	Techniques for administering salt water to children
Aventis	page 426	Pentacel vaccine against 5 diseases
Merck Frosst	page 428	Varivax III vaccine against chicken pox
Fondation Universitas du Canada	page 475	Registered education savings plan and contest coupon

Catherine Brochu, Advertising Representative (418) 694-2363